REACHING
FOR THE
STARS

THE ILLUSTRATED HISTORY
OF MANNED SPACEFLIGHT

PETER BOND

CASSELL

To
Mary Arrowsmith
and
Jack Drury

Cassell
Wellington House
125 Strand
London WC2R 0BB

First published 1994
Revised and updated 1996

Distributed in the United States
by Sterling Publishing Co., Inc.
387 Park Avenue South, New York, NY 10016-8810

Distributed in Australia
by Capricorn Link (Australia) Pty Ltd
2/13 Carrington Road, Castle Hill, NSW 2154

British Library Cataloguing-in-Publication Data
A catalogue record for this book is available from the British Library

ISBN 0-304-34797-3

Typeset by Litho Link Limited, Welshpool, Powys, Wales
Printed and bound in Hong Kong

CONTENTS

Scientist-astronaut Harrison H. Schmitt working at the Lunar Roving Vehicle near Apollo 17's Moon landing site, December 1972. (Eugene Cernan/NASA)

FOREWORD

*by Apollo 17 Astronaut
Harrison Schmitt*

Danger, excitement, opportunity, knowledge and beauty await the children of Earth as they travel through the new ocean of space and settle on lunar and planetary shores. Peter Bond's *Reaching for the Stars* provides the historical basis for this clear message from the first third of a century of the Space Age.

Over 35 years have passed since Sputnik's shocking demonstration that the Space Age had begun. A decade later, in 1968, hundreds of millions of people throughout the world simultaneously found inspiration in Apollo 8's Christmas Eve message from the Moon. Then, on 20 July 1969, the world held its collective breath until humankind touched the plains around Tranquillity Base. No events in history have demonstrated so profound a change in the technological, indeed the evolutionary, status of humankind.

The people of the world have viewed this remarkable period of space-related accomplishment, competition and sacrifice against a kaleidoscopic backdrop of cold war, democratic revolution, technological change and environmental risk.

Now, space has become Earth's grand stage for the Third Millennium – a stage of infinite challenge for human action, imagination and creative spirit. Scripts that meet the challenge of finding alternative energy sources will be written there, probably including the helium fusion resources of the Moon. Actors on this stage will also play out the next great human adventure, the settlement of Mars. These actors, the parents of the first Martians, live among us today.

Waiting beyond the first Martians are those who will journey to the stars. Indeed, reaching for the stars no longer exceeds our grasp.

H.S.
Albuquerque

INTRODUCTION

It seems hard to comprehend that the Space Race is over. For almost half a century, the post-war world was dominated by the United States and the Soviet Union. Now the Soviet Union no longer exists, and the Commonwealth of Independent States is but a pale imitation of the Soviet superpower which led the world into the Space Age.

In 1957 the Cold War was at its peak. The steppes of Kazakhstan trembled as yet another Soviet ballistic missile took to the skies from a secret cosmodrome. But this was no ordinary test flight. Perched in the nose of the needle-like rocket was a small metal sphere which would change the world. Its name was Sputnik.

Not only did the first artificial satellite inaugurate the Space Age, but it heralded the Space Race, a period of intense rivalry between the two superpowers. As so often in human history, the driving forces behind the race to dominate space were the military-industrial complexes, each of which intended to grab the strategically important high ground before the other.

In a world riven by ideological differences and political rivalries, propaganda points played a significant role in determining space policies. If the Soviets launched an artificial satellite, it was essential that the United States be seen to do the same. If the United States expressed its intention to deliver a man into orbit or to land on the Moon, the Soviet leadership demanded that their scientists reach the landmark first.

For seven and a half years, the Soviets chalked up a remarkable series of space triumphs: the first satellite, the first pictures of the Moon's far side, the first man in space, the first woman in space, the first duo and trio in space, and the first spacewalk.

With hindsight, it is easy to see how the West was duped into believing in the superiority of Soviet technology. In fact, the early Soviet lead in the Space Race was largely a result of three factors. In order to deliver their large, heavy nuclear warheads to European or American soil, the Soviet military required a powerful ballistic missile. The Soviet government was prepared to provide all the money and facilities necessary to meet that aim. It just happened that the genius behind the design of these missiles was also a believer in the peaceful exploration of space. Sergei Korolev was the man with the vision to organize an innovative design bureau with the express purpose of launching satellites, and then men, into Earth orbit.

Against this background, the United States presented a disunited front, despite the availability of the German design team who had produced the V-2 rocket used to pulverize London during the Second World War. Money and expertise were spread among the three branches of the armed forces, and the result was an embarrassing series of explosions in full public view.

It was against this depressing background that President Kennedy was able to channel American pride and patriotism into a bold, almost foolhardy, endeavour. On 25 May 1961, he committed his nation to a race to land the first man on the Moon before the end of the decade. The risks he and his advisers were taking can be illustrated by the fact that the total flight duration for American astronauts up to that time added up to a mere 15 minutes and 22 seconds. Another nine months were to pass before John Glenn became the first American to orbit the planet.

Out of that national commitment, unprecedented in peace-time, came the Apollo programme, still seen by space officials and ordinary people alike as the zenith of American space achievements. At a cost of $25 billion and the lives of three astronauts, millions of people were able to witness history in the making as Neil Armstrong's ghostly image flitted across their TV screens, then gingerly hopped from the bottom rung of the Lunar Module ladder and into the history books.

Over two decades have passed since man last

set foot on our neighbouring world in December 1972. Today, it is fashionable to criticize the Apollo extravaganza. Twelve men walked on the Moon, and six of them drove a battery-powered car over the grey, dusty lunar plains. 'To what end?' ask the critics. Was it really worth all that expenditure and effort so that 800 lb (364 kg) of rocks could be brought back to Earth for analysis? The answer to that question is obviously, 'No.' But to ask that question is to misunderstand the rationale behind Apollo. Above all, it was about national prestige, about patriotism, about the competition between two totally contrasting ideologies and two alien political systems.

Apollo proved that the American system and American technology were still the best in the world. Morale among employees of aerospace companies and NASA alike has never been as high. Even before the Moon landings came to their triumphant conclusion in 1972, the Nixon administration had lost interest in space and cut back on the NASA budget. Although it was agreed to build a cheaper, semi-reusable Space Shuttle, the modular space station which it was to serve lay on the scrap heap.

The years since the return of Apollo 17 have been a time of financial retrenchment and public disillusion. In the depressed conditions of today, it is hardly surprising that Apollo is seen as the most successful and significant programme of the Space Age.

The American space programme has never recovered from the cutbacks of the 1970s and 1980s. Unbearable pressure on hardware and employees alike caused overwork, sloppiness and fatigue to take their toll in the worst ever launch disaster. The loss of Challenger and her crew of seven grounded the Shuttle for more than two years.

The situation in the former Soviet Union is even worse. After decades of state subsidies and massive investment in the defence sector, the space industry has no capital and no unified leadership. Under pressure to provide financial returns on investment, the various enterprises are trying desperately to raise hard currency by offering for sale anything and everything. Former state secrets are now being offered on the open market. It remains to be seen what can be salvaged from the ruins of the planet's first space nation.

Even in isolationist America, times are changing. Europeans, Japanese and Russians are increasingly being seen as potential partners rather than rivals for the High Frontier. Politicians and scientists are at last beginning to contemplate a long-term strategy in which representatives of different nations may share space station facilities, colonize the Moon, and explore the rust-red deserts of Mars.

Perhaps this may turn out to be the really valuable legacy of space exploration for the future of our tiny, vulnerable world, that peoples may lay down the sword and take up the spirit of friendship and co-operation as they work together in a quest to reach for the stars.

This account would not have been possible without the help of numerous friends and colleagues. It is impossible to thank everyone, but I must mention Harrison Schmitt for contributing the foreword, and Simon Tuite of Cassell, who brought this project to fruition.

I have used many sources of information, including numerous NASA publications, *Spaceflight*, the monthly magazine published by the British Interplanetary Society, and the late, lamented, *Spaceflight News*. Thanks also go to Brian Hooper, author of the *Cosmonaut Team*, to Ralph Gibson and Theo Russell at Novosti, and to Rex Hall.

One of the strengths of the book is the quality and variety of illustrations. Valuable help in obtaining these was provided by staff at NASA HQ, Lisa Malone at Johnson Space Centre, Anne-Marie Laborde at CNES, Nicholas L. Johnson at Teledyne Brown Engineering, David Montgomery and Cathy Rice at Space Commerce Corporation, Theo Pirard, Ralph Gibbons, Chris Hayes at Moscow Narodny Bank, Yvonne Walther at DLR and Captain William Dickens of the US Army.

Finally, I must mention my wife, Edna, without whose patient forbearance this book would never have been written.

1
LIVING IN SPACE

As far as we know, Earth is the only refuge for life forms in the entire universe. Since the creation of our planet 4,500 million years ago, life has evolved to fill even the most inhospitable and unpromising niches: bubbling, sulphurous hot springs, the dark depths of the ocean, the frozen wastes of Antarctica. Birds and insects have even conquered the air. Yet there is one environment which is so hostile that no life form has evolved to occupy it – the vacuum of outer space.

This was the barrier faced in the late 1950s and early 1960s by the doctors and engineers of the United States and the Soviet Union. Their goal was no less than the human conquest of space.

THE SELECT FEW

Most ordinary mortals would shrink in fear at the thought of sitting 100 feet (30 m) above the ground on top of a glorified Roman candle and waiting for the touch paper to be lit. Yet this is exactly the ordeal faced by anyone who intends to leave planet Earth. Add the fact that the orbiting spacecraft will be travelling at the unimaginable speed of 17,500 mph (28,000 kmph) – or, put more starkly, five miles (8 km) a second – and it becomes eminently clear that only a special kind of person volunteers to be an astronaut.

In both the United States and the Soviet Union, there was considerable doubt whether humans would be able to survive the stresses of space travel. There was also a major debate concerning the necessary personal qualities and professional expertise of the ideal candidates.

Submariners, mountain climbers and parachutists all had their supporters, but eventually the military pilots won the day through their recognized abilities to control a rapidly moving aircraft at high altitudes and to adapt to sudden deviations from the flight programme. The chiefs of the armed forces also presented a strong argument that a military presence in space was necessary since it was vital to control the high ground in a potential new battlefield.

In the Soviet Union, the first cosmonauts were all Air Force pilots under the command of Lieutenant General Nikolai Kamanin. It was a similar story in the United States, where seven military pilots were chosen for the Mercury programme in April 1959. Three of them were from the Air Force, three from the Navy Air Force, and there was one Marine pilot named John Glenn.

This apparent dominance of the military in the American manned space programme is, however, only partially accurate. Space policy changed on 1 October 1958 when President Eisenhower created the civilian National Aeronautics and Space Administration (NASA), ensuring a lead role for those who favoured the peaceful exploration of space.

The US Air Force continued to pursue its own projects to send men into space. The Dyna-Soar programme, intended to launch a small delta-winged glider on top of a Titan 3 rocket, ran from 1958 till 1963. A plan to use a modified Gemini spacecraft as a Manned Orbiting Laboratory was similarly cancelled in 1968 when the astronauts in training transferred over to NASA.

On both sides of the Iron Curtain, the selection procedure was almost brutal in its thoroughness. In the Soviet Union the original army of 3,000 volunteers was ruthlessly cut down to the final group of 20. In America, the task was simplified by fewer applications – 508 – for fewer seats.

One reason for the difference in the number of applicants was the much stricter criteria applied in the States. Any would-be astronaut had to be under 40 years old, less than 5 ft 11 in (1.8 m) tall, in excellent physical condition, hold a Bachelor's degree or equivalent, be a qualified jet and test pilot, and have a minimum overall flying time of 1,500 hours.

There were only two test pilot schools in the entire country, one for the Navy at Patuxent River in Maryland, the other at Edwards Air Force Base in California. Not everyone was in favour of imitating a 'man in a can'. Chuck Yeager, first man to break the sound barrier, commented, 'I wouldn't want to sweep off monkey shit before I sat in the capsule.'

In the Soviet Union, the very large spacecraft enabled even more automation. Indeed, the fear that the pilot might panic during the flight led to the introduction of a 'logical lock' on the first Vostok flights. The cosmonaut could not switch to manual control unless he opened a special envelope and punched in a secret code, 1-2-5 in Gagarin's case.

The cosmonauts selected in 1959 were young, fit Air Force pilots with an upper age limit of 30. Their physical characteristics were determined by the size of the spacecraft – maximum height was 5 ft 7 in (1.7 m) and top weight 154 lb (70 kg).

The Mercury Seven. Back row, left to right: *Alan B. Shepard Jr, Virgil I. 'Gus' Grissom, L. Gordon Cooper.* Front row, left to right: *Walter M. Schirra Jr, Donald K. 'Deke' Slayton, John H. Glenn Jr, and M. Scott Carpenter.* (NASA)

They were considerably less experienced than their American counterparts. Gagarin, for example, had only 230 flying hours under his belt, Titov had 240 and Leonov 250, with only about 900 hours for the most experienced in the group. They also had little, if any, parachute experience – Gagarin had completed five jumps at the time of his selection.

SPREADING THE NET WIDER

Later in the 1960s, older, more experienced pilots were recruited alongside engineers, scientists and doctors. Valentina Tereshkova became the first woman to fly in space in 1963. Boris Yegorov became the first doctor to experience orbital weightlessness a year later. Alongside him in Voskhod 1 was the first civilian engineer, Konstantin Feoktistov.

NASA was slower to bring in civilians, with the first two recruited in 1963. One of them – Neil Armstrong – was to become a household name only six years later. Gradually the criteria were widened and the intense scrutiny relaxed a little. The advent of the Shuttle with its lower acceleration loads on the crew meant that space flight was no longer restricted to a few superfit specimens. In 1990, 59-year-old Vance Brand became the oldest person ever to enter space, an achievement which demonstrates the remarkable changes during the past 30 years.

The Shuttle has opened the door for women in the US space programme. The first recruits were selected in 1978 as part of a new astronaut category, the mission specialists. They are responsible for most of the Shuttle operations outside piloting the craft. A third group, the payload specialists, has specialist knowledge of the satellite or equipment carried on a dedicated Shuttle mission. They are often selected by the companies which provide payloads, although they have to meet minimum NASA health requirements.

GETTING BENEATH THE SKIN

The first recruits had to undergo an ordeal comparable to any venture into space. Before final selection, an army of doctors and psycho-logists probed every corner of the candidates' minds and bodies in a relentless search for a minute weakness.

Among the fiendish inventions they had to endure were vacuum chambers in which no sound could be heard or where the temperature varied rapidly from freezing to boiling, altitude chambers which simulated the rarefied air on the highest mountains, centrifuges which swung round the occupant so fast that his face was twisted out of shape, and bone-jarring vibration stands.

The Mercury astronauts faced a bewildering variety of tests. Every organ, muscle and nerve was probed. The doctors measured body fat levels, sperm count, heartbeat, brainwaves and blood composition. There were 17 different eye tests. They were submerged in water, walked on treadmills, climbed repeatedly on and off a 20 inch (50 cm) step, and rode a wheel-less bicycle on which the brake was tightened at regular intervals. When the pulse peaked at 180 a minute, they were checked to see how quickly they returned to normal.

A wide range of temperatures can be found in space, so the doctors put them inside a heat chamber and baked them for two hours. They then took the opposite track and told the guinea pigs to put their feet in buckets of ice water for minutes at a time.

Meanwhile the psychologists did their worst. There were 600 questions on the personality tests alone. Then candidates were asked to complete the sentence, 'I am . . .' 20 times and there was the famous ink-blot test in which the candidate had to say what he thought about when confronted by a pattern of splodges on a piece of paper. Some of the answers were eye-opening, if not downright obscene!

Things were little different in the Soviet Union. Before his epic spacewalk, Alexei Leonov had to endure several weeks in an isolation chamber, then a thermal chamber and a decompression chamber. Immediately afterwards, he was taken to the airport, put on a plane, and obliged to parachute back to Earth. The doctors justified such treatment by saying that they needed to know whether his mind would be affected by an abrupt change from a confined room to the boundlessness of space.

The Chief Designer surrounded by the first cosmonauts. Front row, left to right: *Popovich, Gorbatko, Khrunov, Gagarin, Chief Designer Sergei Korolev, Korolev's wife with Popovich's daughter, Karpov (training director), Nikitin (parachute trainer), Fedorov (doctor).* Middle row: *Leonov, Nikolayev, Rafikov, Zaikin, Volynov, Titov, Nelyubov, Bykovsky, Shonin.* Back row: *Filatyev, Anikeyev, Belyayev. Missing from the picture are Komarov, Varlamov, Kartashov and Bondarenko.* (Novosti)

EARLY CASUALTIES

Although Sergei Korolev, the Chief Designer of Soviet spacecraft, insisted on a large group of cosmonauts, it soon became clear that this was impractical. On 30 May 1960, a select group of six men was chosen for intensive flight training. Their names were Anatoli Kartashov, Valentin Varlamov, Yuri Gagarin, Gherman Titov, Andrian Nikolayev and Pavel Popovich.

Two of these dropped out of the reckoning even before the first Vostok launch. On 24 July Varlamov dislocated the vertebrae in his neck while diving into a lake and was obliged to take a desk job on the programme. Later that year, Kartashov suffered haemorrhages on the spine after enduring 8g on the centrifuge, and was sent back to his work as a test pilot.

Another casualty was the youngest of the cosmonauts, 24-year-old Valentin Bondarenko. He died in a horrifying accident just a few weeks before Gagarin's momentous voyage. Having successfully come through his ten-day stint inside an isolation chamber, the delighted young man removed his biosensors and wiped himself with cotton wool. Then, without looking, he threw it away. It landed on an electric heater, and in a matter of seconds the oxygen-rich atmosphere in the chamber caused an inferno. The young trainee was quickly enveloped in flame. He died eight hours later from the severe burns. For the next 25 years, Bondarenko's name and the circumstances of his death remained a state secret.

Two Mercury astronauts also learned what it was like to be grounded for medical reasons. Deke Slayton was all set for America's second orbital flight aboard Mercury 7 when his flight status was suddenly withdrawn just 10 weeks before the scheduled launch. Three years of waiting and four months of intensive training came to nothing when NASA Administrator James Webb decided that he could not ignore a slight heart murmur detected during a centrifuge test in August 1959.

Just two years after his historic maiden flight, Alan Shepard also suffered the indignity of being grounded, this time for an inner ear infection which caused dizziness. Both he and Slayton accepted desk jobs until they were eventually cleared and returned to flight status.

Spaceflight can be dangerous! This Mercury capsule was recovered from the sea bed after an Atlas booster blew up one minute after launch on 29 July 1960. There was no escape tower attached to the unmanned capsule. (NASA)

Curiously, for such a dangerous occupation, more astronauts have been injured or killed in mundane accidents than during actual flights. Theodore 'Ted' Freeman died when his T-38 twin-seat training aircraft ran into a flock of snow geese. He tried to eject but there was insufficient height for his parachute to open fully before he plunged into the ground.

The crew of Gemini 9, Elliott See and Charles Bassett, lost their way in poor visibility over the McDonnell factory at St Louis. Their aircraft struck the building which contained the spacecraft they were due to fly, then ploughed into a nearby car park and exploded in a giant fireball.

Clifton Curtis Williams died when his T-38 suddenly went out of control and plunged into a wood near Tallahassee. The short career of Edward Givens came to an untimely end when his Volkswagen car crashed into a ditch.

Most shocking of all was the incineration of Gus Grissom, Edward White and Roger Chaffee during a routine ground simulation inside the first Apollo Command Module. The men died within seconds from inhalation of smoke and the effects of the intense heat which burned through their pressure suits.

SAFETY FIRST

Despite a number of close calls, remarkably few people have met their deaths during a mission. The space casualty list so far contains four cosmonauts who died during re-entry of early Soyuz craft, and seven astronauts who died in the explosion of the Space Shuttle Challenger just 73 seconds after launch.

No rocket yet built has achieved a 100 per cent success rate. For a typical modern booster, engineers would expect a launch failure about once every 20 to 25 flights – not very good odds for a human passenger!

Experience has proved that the most hazardous parts of a space voyage occur at launch and during re-entry. Various methods have been introduced in an effort to improve safety. If an emergency arises prior to ignition, crews are expected to evacuate the spacecraft and use a slide wire basket to carry them 1,200 feet (360 m) into an underground bunker.

The most commonly used method of saving lives during launch mishaps is the rocket propelled escape system, first used on the Mercury flights of the early 1960s. This small solid fuel rocket was designed to fire for little more than a second, just sufficient to pull the capsule away from the booster in a sudden emergency. Once the craft reached a safe altitude, a parachute would automatically deploy to bring it safely back for a splashdown not far from the launch pad.

A similar system was used on the Saturn Moon rockets, and an escape tower is used to this day on all Soviet manned Soyuz rockets. Several cosmonauts have cause to be thankful that the escape tower has functioned perfectly when it has been called upon.

The other main alternative is the ejection seat. The Soviets provided such a seat for their first cosmonauts, although for many years they denied that Gagarin ended his flight by bailing out. This system provided both a means of escape during launch and a safe way of landing.

Ejection seats were first used on American spacecraft for the two-man Gemini of the mid-1960s. A rocket catapult (rocat) was developed which had the capability of throwing an astronaut a distance of 1,000 feet (330 m) from an exploding Titan booster in six seconds. A small hybrid balloon-parachute called a ballute acted as a stabilizer.

More recently, the American Space Shuttle carried ejection seats on its first two-man test flights, but they were not feasible for use by larger crews and were removed from STS-5 onwards. The Soviets have also developed ejection seats for the first manned flights of their Buran Shuttle.

After the loss of the Shuttle Challenger, the Presidential inquiry called for a new crew escape system for use after the solid rocket boosters had stopped firing. Since the 26th Shuttle mission, there has been provision for crew to slide out along a telescopic pole once it has been deployed outside the vehicle. A full crew of eight can be evacuated in two minutes.

It is worth noting that not all spacecraft have been provided with launch escape systems. Neither of the Voskhod craft which flew during 1964–65 carried ejection seats or escape towers!

DESIGNING A SPACECRAFT

Any crewed space vehicle requires a lot of excess baggage simply to keep its occupants alive. Even America's first manned spacecraft, the small, unsophisticated Mercury capsule, contained thousands of parts and seven miles (11 km) of electrical wiring. Modern rockets and spacecraft are assembled from millions of parts made by numerous manufacturers and assembled by a team of contractors and subcontractors. Even assuming a 0.1 per cent failure rate for a Saturn V rocket, there would still be 3,000 parts which malfunctioned on each flight!

Back-up systems had to be provided wherever possible. In addition, there had to be a store of consumables such as air, food and water. All of this meant that a manned spaceship had to weigh several times more than a robot ship, making it harder to lift off the ground and much more expensive to operate.

Sometimes, spacecraft designers came up with risky engineering solutions. On the Apollo missions, for example, the lunar lander was built with only one engine for blasting off from the Moon. A malfunction in the engine would condemn the astronauts to a lingering death a quarter of a million miles from home.

BREATHING IN A VACUUM

Since there is no air in space, the crew have to bring it from Earth. Unfortunately, this supply soon begins to run out, since each person uses about 2 lb (0.9 kg) of oxygen per day. A small amount of leakage from the spacecraft also has to be taken into account.

The approach to this problem has differed in America and the USSR. Soviet spacecraft contain a 'normal' atmosphere of oxygen and nitrogen at 14.7 psi (pounds per square inch) pressure while most American craft have used pure oxygen at 5 psi. The US alternative originated in order to reduce weight because of the limitations of their early boosters.

Things began to change with the low pressure mixture of 70 per cent oxygen and 30 per cent nitrogen chosen for Skylab, and NASA

Interior view of a Mercury capsule. Note the maze of wiring and cramped conditions. (Science Museum)

eventually switched to a normal atmosphere on the Space Shuttle.

Both systems have their disadvantages. Despite use of flame-resistant materials, pure oxygen is a major fire hazard. On the other hand, a mixed gas atmosphere means that nitrogen absorbed in the blood and body tissues will form bubbles when the air pressure suddenly falls. Spacewalkers have to spend about an hour breathing pure oxygen before it is safe for them to venture outside in their low pressure suits.

American space missions have tended to be relatively short in duration, so they have always carried their own oxygen supply. On Skylab, for example, this life-sustaining gas was replenished from tanks of liquid oxygen. In order to reduce dependence on the lifeline from Earth, the Soviets use oxides and superoxides of alkali metals such as potassium to generate oxygen for their space stations.

The removal of harmful waste gases such as the carbon dioxide breathed out by the crew is just as vital. This is done by using a variety of filters and chemical absorbents such as lithium hydroxide which have to be replaced at regular intervals.

WALKING IN SPACE

If humans want to work in the vacuum of space, they need the protection afforded by a pressure suit. Early space suits were based on the versions worn by high altitude test pilots. By the early 1970s, they had improved so much that the Apollo astronauts were able to enjoy up to eight hours outside their spacecraft exploring the lunar surface.

Although its internal pressure is only 3.5 to 4 psi, the air inside the suit consists of pure oxygen, so an astronaut wearing a pressure suit actually has more oxygen to breathe than he would at sea level wearing his normal clothes. Oxygen circulating inside a gastight nylon bladder also prevents fogging of the helmet visor and removes exhaled carbon dioxide to filters in the backpack or in the spacecraft if a tether is used.

Unfortunately, movement of the body, and particularly delicate finger manipulation, is very difficult once the suit is pressurized. Various methods have been tried to improve astronaut mobility, ranging from pulleys to cables and bearings, but with limited success.

In earlier programmes, pressure suits were tailor-made for each astronaut. The latest Shuttle suits for extravehicular activity (EVA) are unisex and come in three sizes. To make dressing easier, the astronaut climbs into the 'trouser' section first, then dons the hard upper torso. The two pieces snap together with sealing rings.

Soviet pressure suits are one-piece and the cosmonaut has to clamber into the suit through a 'door' in the rear of the aluminium shell which protects the upper body. The life support systems are attached to this 'door', which can be swung closed once the cosmonaut has squeezed into the suit. Adjustment straps on the arms and legs are used to provide a fairly snug fit for any crew member. The latest Soviet suits are designed for ten missions of up to six hours each.

Maintaining a comfortable body temperature requires a combination of insulation and heat redistribution. Spacewalking astronauts are protected by a network of tiny water-filled tubes sewn into an undergarment resembling a pair of longjohns. Body heat is transferred by the water to the backpack and then radiated into space.

Insulation and protection against micrometeorites are provided by numerous layers of materials such as teflon and glass fibre. Gloves and helmets are clipped onto the suit to provide a pressure seal.

Mercury and Gemini helmets were close-fitting and rotated with the crewman's head, but the Apollo and Shuttle helmets are fixed, allowing free head movement. On Soviet suits, the body and helmet are made of a single metal structure. An outer visor is worn over the helmet to shield the astronaut against micrometeorites as well as damaging ultraviolet and infra-red radiation from the Sun.

Until recently astronauts have been unable to move far from their spacecraft. They had to be linked to their craft by a lifeline to prevent them from drifting away into the vast emptiness of space.

This began to change with the introduction of a jet-propelled backpack called the Manned Manoeuvring Unit (MMU) in 1984. Bruce McCandless put on an astonishing show of space acrobatics in the first ever display of free flying in space. The armchair-like MMU enables the occupant to move up to 330 feet (100 m) from the Shuttle by propelling compressed nitrogen gas from 24 tiny jets. The 300 lb (135 kg) unit carries sufficient oxygen and electrical power to supply the astronaut for up to seven hours.

In January 1990, the Soviets unveiled their version of the 'space motorcycle' in a series of test flights outside the Mir space station. It is slightly heavier than the American model, has 32 thrusters and uses compressed air as propellant.

Climbing into a Shuttle EVA suit. The top part of the suit and its portable backpack are attached to the wall on the Shuttle mid-deck. (NASA)

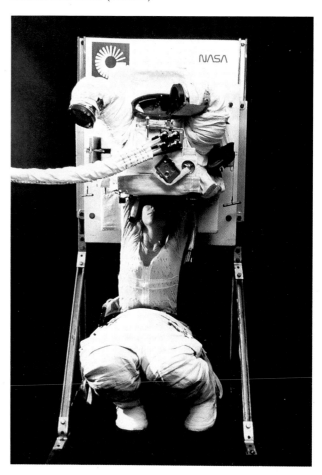

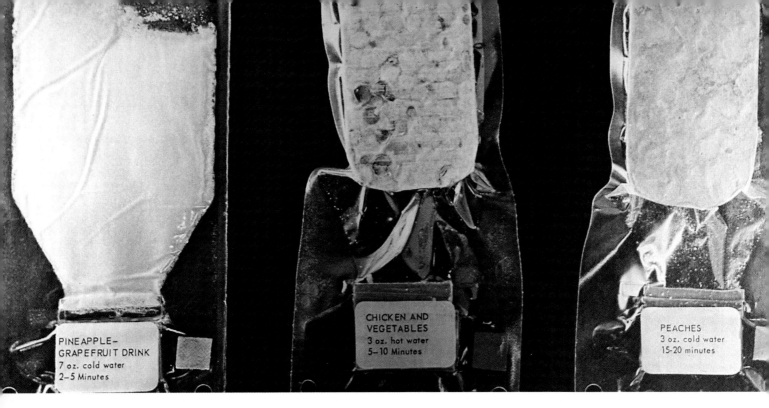

Labels visible in image:

PINEAPPLE-
GRAPEFRUIT DRINK
7 oz. cold water
2-5 Minutes

CHICKEN AND
VEGETABLES
3 oz. hot water
5-10 Minutes

PEACHES
3 oz. cold water
15-20 minutes

EATING OUT

In space, the simple task of eating and drinking is complicated by the fact that food and liquids tend to float around the cabin, with potentially disastrous effects on electrical systems.

Prior to the early flights, doctors and dieticians spent long hours devising menus and worrying whether astronauts would be able to swallow. Later on, the crew members were free to select their own meal combinations, as long as they added up to 2,800 calories a day and fulfilled the nutritional requirements.

There was also the problem of how best to package their culinary delights. Early space food was stored in toothpaste-type tubes, though some variations were accepted. Gherman Titov, for example, was allowed a few small chunks of bread and some vitamin-enriched peas in addition to his tubes of meat purée and jam. Popovich, the pilot of Vostok 4, progressed to a breakfast of sausage, sandwiches and cherry juice.

The diet of the Mercury astronauts was equally unappetizing, but at least they had a good send-off with a two-pound steak for breakfast. Apart from soft food in tubes, the astronauts were given freeze-dried food which had to be rehydrated before it could be squeezed out, and bite-size cubes.

Things began to improve as spacecraft grew in size and water became available. The aluminium

Space food used on the Apollo Moon missions. To make these freeze-dried foods edible, a measured amount of hot or cold water was squirted into the packet, the contents were kneaded until they formed a thick paste, then they were squeezed from the packet directly into the mouth.
(Peter Bond)

tubes were replaced by plastic, and a special 'water gun' was used to rehydrate the freeze-dried items. Enough varieties of dishes were available to give menu selections for four days. A typical menu might include shrimp cocktail, chicken and vegetables, toast squares, butterscotch pudding and apple juice.

Crews on the Apollo missions were given the added luxury of heated water for hot food and drinks. One notable innovation was the spoon bowl, whose contents could be rehydrated then eaten with a spoon.

On Skylab, the larder held up to 72 different food items; food such as filet mignon and ice cream could be stored in a freezer while chilled fruits and drinks were kept in a refrigerator. The large American and Soviet space stations also have room for a heated dining table.

The US Space Shuttle goes one step further with a convection oven. Heating and reconstitution of a full meal for four takes up to one hour. Crews are able to eat from aluminium cans with full pull-out lids. These are held in place on trays by a slit plastic surround. Knife, fork and spoon are held to the table magnetically.

Soviet long-duration flights have only been made possible by a convoy of unmanned Progress supply ships. These arrive every few months with fresh supplies of food, spare parts and mail from home. One curious side-effect of extended weightlessness is the deadening of the taste buds, so that even favourite dishes come to resemble a mouthful of sawdust. Not surprisingly, sauces, spices, onions and garlic are among the most keenly awaited items.

Attempts to grow food in space are still at an early stage. Experiments with plants using a rotating centrifuge have generally led to failure, although cosmonauts have succeeded in cultivating radishes and lettuce on board the Mir station.

Rearing animals in orbit is also proving a difficult task. During 1990, eight out of 48 quail eggs were successfully hatched in a special incubator on board Mir, but the chicks were unable to adapt to zero gravity and all of them perished within a few days.

SPACE HYGIENE

In the limited confines of a spacecraft, waste disposal becomes of utmost importance. Simply dumping it overboard is a common solution, but the debris can come back to haunt you. Many an astronaut has been heard to complain that navigational sightings have been complicated by swarms of water or urine droplets sparkling in the viewfinder like a myriad stars. There is also increasing concern that even the tiniest flake of paint or ice can turn into a potential death threat when travelling at 17,000 mph (28,000 kmph).

Many of the earlier craft simply filled up with bags of discarded food wrappers, faeces and urine as the mission progressed. Gemini 7 astronaut Jim Lovell commented:

We spent many hours prior to the flight finding little spots and crevices in the spacecraft where we could pack things. We would eat three meals a day, and Frank [Borman] would very nicely pack the containers in a small bag and at the end of the day he would throw it behind the seat. We managed to get nine days' debris behind those seats.

In the vast expanse of the Skylab space station, the empty oxygen tank located below the workshop was available for waste accumulation. Everything from empty food cartons to soiled clothes and bags of body wastes was dumped in this giant repository.

For the past 15 years, the Soviets have used the automatic Progress supply craft as a mobile waste disposal system. Once its cargo is unloaded, the ferry is filled with waste and ordered to burn up on re-entry.

Since one person drinks about 6 lb (2.7 kg) of water a day, it follows that a two-person crew would consume 168 lb (76 kg) over a two-week mission. Fortunately, modern technology has eased the problem of water supply in space. Water vapour in the cabin atmosphere can be condensed out by cooling coils, then treated and reused. In addition, fuel cells first used on the Gemini craft produce water as they generate electricity by chemically combining oxygen and hydrogen.

Soviet cosmonauts have enjoyed the luxury of a weekly shower on their space stations for many years, but Skylab was the only American craft to have this facility. The astronaut simply floated into the collapsible cylinder, pulled it up around him and sealed it. Water was then squirted onto his body by means of a hand-held shower head, and airflow, instead of gravity, carried the water downwards. Drying off with a vacuum machine, however, was a laborious, time-consuming occupation, and some astronauts preferred the traditional washcloths. Over 800 were provided, each one colour coded to identify its user.

Astronauts on the week-long Shuttle missions have to settle for sponge baths and a wash basin. Excess water is drawn into a waste tank which is regularly emptied overboard when it becomes full.

The suction effect of airflow has also been used on the Skylab and Shuttle toilets. Solid waste is drawn by a fan into a lower compartment where it is dried and disinfected. Liquid wastes are drawn into a contoured cup and flexible hose and then pumped into a waste tank.

On a number of Shuttle flights, this technological marvel has often become clogged, and the crew have had to resort to the time-honoured method of collecting faeces in special plastic bags, adding a packet of germicide, and sealing them. On one such occasion, a Shuttle crewman was heard to comment, 'We decided those Apollo astronauts must have been real men!'

THE SPACE GYMNASIUM

Right up to Gagarin's voyage, the ability of the human organism to adapt and work in zero gravity was in serious doubt. These fears were reinforced when cosmonaut number two, Gherman Titov, complained of dizziness and nausea during his 17-orbit flight. Such discomfort was avoided on early American flights, but space motion sickness surfaced on the much larger Apollo craft. The problem occurred when astro-

Soviet cosmonaut Anatoli Artsebarski using the bicycle exercise machine on the Mir space station. (Juno)

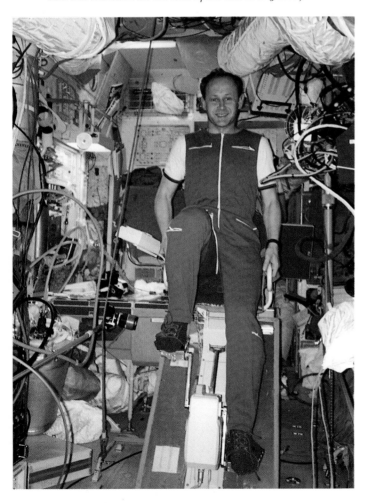

nauts had greater freedom of movement in a more spacious environment. About one-third of all space travellers suffer from this unpleasant sensation during their first week in orbit, after which they tend to adapt to their new circumstances.

Although astronauts find it equally convenient to eat, sleep or work whether floating upright or upside down, disorientation is a problem. In order to give the crew some kind of reference point, space station designers use different shades of paint to differentiate between the 'floor' and the 'ceiling'.

Apart from space sickness, weightlessness generates a number of potentially dangerous physical changes. Among them are loss of weight and dehydration, calcium loss in the bones, weakening of muscles (including the heart), pulse rate variability and decreased red cell and plasma volume in the blood. A particular worry is the effect of gravity when the crew return to Earth. Pooling of blood in the legs, deprivation of blood and oxygen in the brain, and unaccustomed stress on the heart are all dangers to be taken very seriously.

In order to combat these debilitating effects, extra vitamins and calcium are added to the diets of long-term crews. They also carry out a strict exercise regime for two to three hours each day. Apart from simple apparatus such as chest expanders and elastic tension straps, space stations carry a bicycle ergometer and a treadmill. Soviet specialists proudly announced that Yuri Romanenko 'ran' about 625 miles (1,000 km) during his 11-month occupation of Mir.

Cosmonauts also wear a Penguin constant loading suit which forces the body muscles to maintain an upright posture, and Chibis trousers which exert pressure on the legs and force the heart to work harder by pumping more blood from their head and chest.

Many lessons have been learned since the crew of Soyuz 9 had to be carried from their capsule on stretchers after only 18 days in orbit. Yuri Romanenko was able to go for gentle jogs and workouts on the second day after completing 326 days in space. Since then, Vladimir Titov and Manarov have extended the all-time endurance record to an entire year, long enough for a one-way trip to the planet Mars.

2

LIFT-OFF!

INTO ORBIT

The youngsters of today are taught to believe that, given time, science and technology can achieve almost anything. So when they hear about plans to build a spaceplane which can fly from Europe to Australia in four hours, they accept that such a fantasy will soon become reality.

Yet it is only in the last 50 years that the human race has developed the means to conquer gravity and explore the vacuum of outer space. Before the Second World War, space travel was a dream, the stuff of science fiction.

The first leap in understanding came through the theoretical work of a deaf Russian named Konstantin Tsiolkovsky. Even before the maiden aeroplane flight of the Wright brothers, he was spelling out the potential of rockets for interplanetary travel. Aware that most of a rocket's weight would be taken up simply by fuel, he proposed a multistage version which would be able to shed its dead weight as the various sections used up their fuel.

He also saw the benefits of liquid fuels over solid fuels, and one of the combinations he suggested became the basis of modern rocketry: liquid oxygen and liquid hydrogen. By the time he died in 1935, he was convinced that his visions of chains of Earth satellites, space stations and journeys to other planets were practical possibilities for future generations.

One of the reasons for his optimism was the pioneering work by Robert Goddard in America. The young professor from Clark University in Worcester, Massachusetts, worked in secret to build the world's first practical liquid-fuelled rocket. On 16 March 1926, his invention soared to a height of 184 feet (60 m), witnessed only by his wife and two assistants.

Seeing no practical use for his rockets, the United States government ignored his work, and Goddard died almost unnoticed in 1945. It was a different story on the other side of the Atlantic, where Hitler's Germany took an intense interest in the military potential of guided missiles. By 1942, his scientists had succeeded in creating the V-2 ('Vengeance Weapon 2'), which was capable of carrying a bomb a distance of 200 miles (320 km) at a speed faster than that of sound.

As the Allies closed in on Nazi Germany, the rocket scientists, led by Wernher von Braun, surrendered to American troops. They were only too keen to divulge their secrets in return for a secure future under the protective wing of the US government. Their underground assembly plant was ransacked before the Soviets arrived, and parts for 100 V-2s were ferried back to the States for evaluation.

Although there was little left for the Soviets to retrieve from the wreckage, they did find a few rockets and blueprints. Stalin's secret police rounded up and deported several thousand German specialists in rocketry and nuclear physics.

Both superpowers set to work to develop and improve the German technology, spurred on by the knowledge that whoever possessed a battery of nuclear missiles could dominate the world. The US Army set up a V-2 test range at White Sands in New Mexico, and by 1949 the addition of a small Wac Corporal sounding rocket as a second stage enabled the rocket to reach a height of 250 miles (400 km), a record which stood until 1956.

The Soviet missile programme went ahead behind closed doors, led by an anonymous 'Chief Designer'. Sergei Korolev had worked in rocketry since the 1930s, and his weapons had

A US Army V-2 undergoing trials at White Sands in New Mexico. (Dept. of the Army)

introduced in 1956, followed on 21 August 1957 by the successful launch of the R-7, the world's first two-stage intercontinental ballistic missile. Two months later, the Space Age was born as a modified R-7 lifted the world's first artificial satellite into orbit.

For the next 21 days, Sputnik's beep-beep signal reminded the world of the Soviet Union's offensive power and technological supremacy, The United States had been caught napping. Further embarrassment followed when the Navy's Vanguard persisted in blowing up in full view of the public.

In a last ditch effort to save face, the Pentagon turned to von Braun's Army team at Huntsville in Alabama. On 31 January 1958, his modified Jupiter-C rocket succeeded in blasting off from Cape Canaveral and inserting Explorer 1 into orbit. America was up and running. The Space Race had begun.

PAVING THE WAY

The question of a manned spaceflight was first put forward by Korolev in April 1956, more than a year before the launch of Sputnik. He knew that sooner or later humans would leave their planet, and he intended to make that dream a reality. Animals would have to pave the way.

Little time was wasted. A mongrel dog called Laika (Barker) was installed in a sealed cylindrical capsule on board Sputnik 2. An automatic dispenser provided food in the form of a nutritious gelatine, while a rubber reservoir was placed over her hind quarters to collect waste products. Metal chains restricted her movements while allowing her to shift position and stand or sit.

For seven days, sensors attached to Laika sent back data on the dog's response to weightlessness and the results showed beyond doubt that animals could tolerate space travel. Unfortunately, Sputnik was not designed to return safely to Earth, so Laika's pathfinding mission was terminated by an injection of poison.

By the end of 1958 the project to send up a human had been approved, although there was still a debate over whether the initial flights should be suborbital hops rather than the

helped to win the war. Despite imprisonment for 'disloyalty' by Stalin, he gathered a talented array of engineers and scientists who spearheaded the drive towards development of ballistic missiles.

The first Soviet nuclear strategic missile was

more difficult and dangerous orbital ventures.

The basic outline of the mission was easily decided. The size and weight of the new spacecraft were determined by the performance of the booster. Its orbital path had to be below 125 miles (200 km) so that the cosmonaut's life would not be endangered by the newly discovered radiation belts.

The greater orbital drag of the atmosphere at lower altitudes meant the capsule's weight could be cut by omitting a back-up retro-rocket. Even if the engine failed to fire, friction from the upper atmosphere would slow the craft sufficiently for it to re-enter after about ten days. To allow for such a possibility, an adequate supply of food would be stored in the cabin.

Before a human could be risked, several test flights were essential. The first of these, Sputnik 4 (also known as Korabl Sputnik 1), was launched on 15 May 1960. It was equipped with a pressurized cabin and carried a load equivalent to the weight of a cosmonaut, but there was no heatshield.

The test ended in a mishap which would have been fatal to a human occupant. The spacecraft was facing the wrong way when its retro-rockets fired, causing the capsule to move into a higher orbit. It finally re-entered the atmosphere more than five years later.

Sputnik 5 (Korabl Sputnik 2) carried a small zoo. The occupants included two dogs, Strelka (Little Arrow) and Belka (Squirrel), 40 mice, two rats, and 15 flasks full of fruit flies. There were also plants such as spiderwort and chlorella, and samples of skin cells.

After one day in orbit, the capsule separated and parachuted to Earth only six miles (10 km) from the target zone. The container which held the animals was ejected at an altitude of about four and a half miles (7 km) and made a heavy parachute landing at a speed of 18 mph (8 m/sec). It was the first time living creatures had travelled through space and been safely recovered.

The only moment of concern was when Belka began vomiting on the fourth orbit. The possibility of a similar mishap when a human went aloft led to a recommendation that the first manned mission should last only one orbit.

The orbits of the next three test flights were much lower, around 125 miles (200 km) in altitude, in order to ensure orbital decay within the ten-day limit of the life support system. The flight of Sputnik 6 (Korabl Sputnik 3) on 1 December 1960 saw the first major space casualties when the dogs Pchelka (Bee) and Mushka (Little Fly) were burned alive. A fault in the system of solar sensors caused the craft to dive towards Earth at too steep an angle.

Three weeks later, a launch emergency arose when the third stage on the rocket malfunctioned. The escape system separated the descent module and saved the animal occupants from death. This mishap was hidden from the public and only revealed many years later.

Despite these setbacks, a prototype manned craft was ready by the end of the year, and in February 1961 three spacecraft were delivered to Baikonur cosmodrome. Two further test flights during March each carried a dummy pilot and one dog. The designers were finally happy with the overall performance of their capsule.

Among those present at the launch of Sputnik 10 (Korabl Sputnik 5) were six young pilots who were poised to rewrite the history books.

COSMONAUT NUMBER ONE

Preparations for training the first cosmonauts were rather hurried. Only on 11 January 1960 did the Communist Party Central Committee agree to the establishment of a new cosmonaut training centre near Moscow named Zvezdny Gorodok (Star Town). Then, on 24 February, Yevgeni Karpov was appointed head of the centre under General Kamanin.

The cosmonaut recruits eagerly congregated from their air bases all over the Soviet Union in March 1960. Their quarters were still under construction, so the first lectures took place at the Frunze Central Airfield. Apart from lectures about spaceflight and spacecraft systems, the newcomers experienced brief periods of weightlessness on roller-coaster flights by Tu-104 aircraft, and regular sessions of parachute jumping. Unlucky Pavel Belyayev put himself out of the running for the first space flight by breaking his leg during a hard landing.

Then in May, Korolev at last revealed his masterpiece, the Vostok (East) spacecraft. A raw young recruit eagerly volunteered to be the first to try out the strange capsule. His name was Yuri Gagarin.

From then on, an increasing part of their training was spent in a mock-up of the craft, familiarizing themselves with the layout and practising all the flight procedures. On 30 May, an elite group of six cosmonauts was chosen to undergo more intensive preparations.

For some time there was indecision among the designers and doctors over who was best suited to pilot the first Vostok. Each candidate excelled in certain areas, but no one was the outstanding favourite: Volynov was the leading parachutist, Bykovsky performed best in the isolation chamber, Nikolayev had greatest endurance on the centrifuge, and so on.

Gradually the name of Gagarin came to the fore. Even among his peers, the young Senior Lieutenant was accepted as the man most likely. He came across as a calm, self-confident and adaptable character who achieved high ratings in all the psychological and medical examinations.

On 8 April 1961, only four days before blast-off, the final decision was announced at a meeting of the State Commission. General Kamanin declared the Air Force recommendation of 27-year-old Gagarin as pilot with Titov as his back-up.

On the day prior to the launch, the silver-grey Vostok booster was rolled out to the launch pad and erected. That night, the cosmonauts and their doctors were installed in a small wooden cottage only 15 minutes' drive from the launch pad. Two similar cottages were occupied by Korolev and other members of the State Commission. The Chief Designer spent a restless night, not helped by his heart condition. He even crept into the cosmonauts' bedroom, but both were sound asleep despite the attached biosensors.

Karpov had little difficulty rousing them at 5.30 next morning. After a session of exercises and a 'space breakfast' of meat purée, blackcurrant jam and coffee, the State Commission announced that the launch was 'Go'.

Both men were fitted with an array of body

sensors, then helped to dress. First came the woollen undergarment, then the pressure suit, followed by the orange coveralls which would make the cosmonaut easier to spot after landing. Finally, they donned the boots, white communication helmet and metal sealed helmet inscribed CCCP (USSR).

At the pad, Gagarin stepped down from the bus and gave a rousing speech to the assembled multitude, then climbed up the metal ladder to the lift. One final wave to the crowd far below, then he was helped into his contour seat. The 90-minute countdown was halted briefly when one of the hatch contacts failed to register, but the cosmonaut remained calm as he listened to music, checked his instruments and spoke to his fellow cosmonauts.

In the underground bunker, Korolev's deputy, Alexandrovich Voskresensky, peered through a periscope and issued the order to push the ignition button, causing the giant rocket to erupt in a cloud of orange flame and smoke.

At first it hardly seemed to move, then the supporting arms swung open like the petals of a flower, the connecting lines separated and the rocket was free. 'We're off!' came the voice of the world's first spaceman as he accelerated past the tower into a clear blue sky. It was 9.07 am Moscow time, the beginning of a new era in human history.

Gagarin was pressed back into his couch as the rocket accelerated and g forces increased. A brief jolt accompanied separation of the four strap-on boosters, then the protective nose cone separated, allowing his first view of planet Earth through the porthole. The second stage burnt out and fell away, allowing the third stage to

Yuri Gagarin, the first human in space. Seated behind him in the bus is his back-up, Gherman Titov, the second Soviet cosmonaut. (Theo Pirard–Tass)

All Vostok cosmonauts ejected from their capsule and parachuted back to Earth. This painting by Alexei Leonov shows Gagarin after he separated from the descent capsule. (Aurora Art Publishers)

place his craft into orbit. As the engines shut off, the loud roar was replaced by silence.

Vostok was placed in an orbit which varied between 112 miles (181 km) and 203 miles (327 km) above the Earth. The planet flashed past his window as the delighted young man experienced an unprecedented speed of about five miles (8 km) per second.

During the next hour and a half, the cool cosmonaut interspersed his technical reports with brief descriptions of the landscape and weather systems far below. He found it easy to write, though he soon discovered one drawback of zero gravity when he released his pencil and it duly floated out of sight. Unperturbed, he switched over to dictation on tape.

Unknown to the cosmonaut, near panic set in at the Control Centre when he was out of direct contact. The number code 'five' was tapping out to reassure the controllers that all was well.

Then, suddenly, the telegraph tape started showing 'three . . . three'. Everyone went pale as they stared at the numbers. Had something gone drastically wrong? Then the 'fives' reappeared. It later turned out that the blip had been caused by a fault in the lines of communication.

Gagarin watched his rapid progress around the planet on a miniature globe on his instrument panel. At 9.51 am Vostok's orientation system locked onto the Sun as it emerged from Earth's shadow and Gagarin witnessed the wonderful succession of colours which herald a space dawn.

All too soon, it was time to prepare for re-entry. At 10.15 am as Vostok was passing over Africa, the automatic system cut in and ten minutes later the retro-rockets fired to slow the craft. The worst part of the return trip came when Gagarin's spherical capsule refused to separate from the instrument section before it plunged into the atmosphere. Even with the shutters drawn over the portholes, he could see the awesome crimson glow as the spacecraft's exterior reached several thousand degrees, but inside the temperature remained a comfortable

20°C. Fortunately, the cables connecting the two sections burned through, allowing the descent capsule to break free.

Gagarin passed safely through the communications blackout and deceleration forces which peaked at 8g. At an altitude of four miles (6.5 km) the drogue parachute deployed, slowing its descent. Soon after, the hatch door was jettisoned automatically, followed two seconds later by operation of the ejection seat. Gagarin was flung from the capsule and began his separate descent towards the welcoming steppe. At an altitude of two and a half miles (4 km) the ejection seat fell away, leaving the cosmonaut swinging free beneath his parachute.

The capsule, charred by its fiery ordeal, landed not far from a deep ravine. Gagarin's touchdown close by was witnessed by Anna Takhtarova, a forester's wife, and her six-year-old granddaughter Rita. They took some convincing that Gagarin was really a Russian spaceman, but they were soon joined by a group of tractor drivers who knew all about his exploits. A lorry load of soldiers appeared on the scene to help remove his pressure suit and inform him that he had already been promoted to Major.

The delighted cosmonaut was given a quick medical, then whisked away by helicopter to be debriefed and to recuperate. In the months to come, the quiet, unassuming carpenter's son became an instant celebrity on a sensational world tour, and the ultimate symbol of Communist achievement.

Many of the mission details remained a secret. Gagarin was obliged to tell the world that he landed inside his capsule to ensure that his record would be accepted by the International Aeronautical Federation. Any pilot who bailed out before landing could not be deemed to have completed his mission!

WINGS OF MERCURY

The news of Gagarin's triumph dropped like a bombshell in America, where the first orbital flight was still many months away. National prestige was at stake. The only thing to do was to bring forward Alan Shepard's suborbital lob into the Atlantic Ocean.

Everyone's nerves were fraught after bad weather forced a three-day postponement, followed by four holds during the countdown on the morning of 5 May. Although his flight was only to last 15 minutes, four hours passed with the impotent astronaut strapped inside his tiny capsule.

Such an extended session of pre-launch preparations had not been foreseen, so it came as a great surprise to all concerned when Shepard could restrain his bladder no longer and relieved himself in his spacesuit. He then took out his frustration on the dithering ground controllers. 'I'm cooler than you are,' he radioed. 'Why don't you fix your little problem and light this candle?'

All the hesitation and frustration were forgotten as the Redstone carried the 37-year-old US Navy Commander into the blue beyond. He barely had time to test the orientation system and admire the view through his periscope before Freedom 7 began to dive back into the atmosphere. G forces rapidly built up, but the red and white parachute deployed right on time, enabling the tiny capsule to splash down east of the Bahamas.

This modest achievement received rave write-ups in the media. Shepard enjoyed a tickertape reception in New York and a reception at the White House, where he received the Distinguished Service Medal from President Kennedy. Sensing the mood of the nation, Kennedy followed up three weeks later by throwing down a multi-billion-dollar gauntlet to the Soviet Union. His speech publicly committed the country to achieve the goal, 'before this decade is out, of landing a man on the Moon and returning him safely to Earth'.

The second of seven planned suborbital rehearsals was soon ready. Perched on top of the Redstone rocket was 35-year-old Virgil 'Gus' Grissom, a veteran of 100 combat missions in the Korean War.

Grissom's 15-minute flight aboard Liberty Bell 7 proved a copybook follow-up to Shepard's pioneering effort until the splashdown. Then everything went wrong. The capsule's hatch blew prematurely. As water began to pour in, Grissom decided to abandon ship. Unable to lift the capsule because of the weight of water inside, the crew of the recovery helicopter was forced to cut Liberty Bell loose. The spacecraft sank like a stone to the bottom of the ocean.

Gus Grissom was in danger of following it as water seeping into his pressure suit threatened to pull him down. His frantic gestures to a second recovery helicopter were misinterpreted as reassuring waves, and it was an exhausted and relieved astronaut who eventually grabbed the horse-collar harness and was winched aboard. In a state of shock he kept repeating, 'I didn't do anything'.

America's first astronaut, Alan Shepard, is winched aboard a helicopter at the end of his 15-minute sub-orbital flight. (NASA)

Before the subsequent Board of Inquiry, Grissom insisted that the jettisoning of the hatch had been a freak accident. In return, the experts gave evidence that such a mishap had never previously been recorded. Grissom was exonerated, but there was no trip to Washington and no tickertape parade. He later wrote, 'I felt reasonably certain that I wouldn't have a second space flight.' However, he didn't give up hope that a place could still be found for the first astronaut to lose his ship. 'They just couldn't get rid of me,' he wrote, 'so they finally gave up and programmed me into Project Gemini.'

TITOV'S DAY IN SPACE

Only two weeks after Grissom's débâcle, the USSR rubbed salt into the wounds by sending up its second spaceman. Gherman Titov's 17-orbit, 25-hour marathon was much more ambitious than Gagarin's and far beyond anything in the pipeline for the Mercury astronauts.

However, not everything went according to plan. Titov suffered from a breakdown in the heating system which resulted in the cabin temperature plummeting to only 6°C. He also became the first traveller to experience space sickness.

Throughout much of the flight, he complained of slight vertigo and nausea, conditions which worsened when he suddenly moved his head or observed rapidly moving objects. In the absence of gravity the cosmonaut had the illusion of flying upside down. Titov's answer was to go to sleep. Concerned by his condition, doctors on the ground allowed him to oversleep by 35 minutes.

On his return to Earth, specialists reported that Titov was fit and well, although he suffered from inner ear problems for some time after his return. He never flew in space again although he eventually rose to the rank of Colonel-General with a senior desk job at Baikonur.

AMERICA IN ORBIT

Spurred on by Titov's triumph, the NASA hierarchy came under increasing pressure to put an American into orbit. Previous test flights of the Atlas booster had hardly been reassuring, but a successful mission on 29 November 1961 involving a chimpanzee called Enos seemed to clear the way for John Glenn.

The 40-year-old Marine Lieutenant-Colonel had been the back-up for both Shepard and Grissom. He was already a well-known personality and hero of both the Second World War and the Korean War, as well as the holder of the transcontinental speed record.

Frustration set in as the December launch date fell back to January and then February through a combination of bad weather and technical hitches, but the determined astronaut allowed

himself only two days off over Christmas and two more at New Year.

By the time Friendship 7 was finally launched on 20 February 1962, Glenn and his back-up Scott Carpenter had overseen 225 repairs and modifications to the capsule. Carpenter's voice over the intercom spoke for the watching thousands of engineers and millions of Americans: 'God speed, John Glenn.'

'The clock is operating. We're under way,' came Glenn's reassuring reply. Two minutes into the flight, Glenn was able to report the

John Glenn climbs into Friendship 7 prior to America's first orbital flight. (NASA)

successful separation of the two side boosters. Half a minute later, the redundant escape tower was boosted free. Suddenly, the sustainer engines cut off as the spaceship reached orbital velocity, transforming Glenn from six times his normal weight to weightlessness.

As the periscope extended and the hydrogen peroxide jets began to turn the craft into its orbital position, Glenn was able to admire the view back along his flight path. The dead Atlas was lurking about 600 feet (185 m) behind him. He was soon fully occupied with status checks, exercises and descriptions of surface features. About 40 minutes after launch, he attempted to describe a wondrous rainbow-coloured sunset as the craft began its first night pass. 'That was sure a short day,' he told Capcom Gordon Cooper, who was based at the ground station in Western Australia.

Suddenly, the air of normality was replaced by bewilderment on the part of the astronaut and alarm on the ground. 'I am in a big mass of some very small particles that are brilliantly lit up,' came the astronaut's excited voice. As the Sun appeared above the horizon, the 'fireflies' disappeared, only to materialize once more on the next orbit.

Although it was eventually decided that Friendship 7's dazzling companions posed no threat, there were more pressing causes for concern. The automatic orientation system began playing up at the end of the first orbit, forcing Glenn to spend more time using manual control. Shortly after, the Canaveral Control Centre received a telemetry signal which indicated a loose heatshield on the capsule. If this was indeed the case, Glenn would burn up on re-entry.

The astronaut was kept in the dark while the engineers tried to check out the situation. Tests suggested that it was only the switch which was malfunctioning, but Glenn was instructed not to jettison his retro-pack in the hope that it would hold the heatshield in place if the worst fears were realized.

The fiery re-entry began towards the end of the third orbit, bringing a nail-biting 4 minutes and 20 seconds of communications blackout. As the outside temperature reached 5,000°C, Glenn watched blazing chunks of retro-pack fly past

his window. The suspense finally came to an end as his voice came through loud and clear and the suspect landing bag deployed perfectly. Friendship 7 splashed down in the Atlantic close to the destroyer Noa, its occupant unscathed apart from a cut on the knuckles received as he hit the plunger to blow off the hatch.

Although Glenn's 4 hours and 55 minutes in space could not compare with Titov's marathon, national pride had been restored. America had left the starting blocks in the race to the Moon.

Three months later, Malcolm Scott Carpenter attempted a repeat performance. As a result of Deke Slayton's medical disbarment, Carpenter was thrown into the hot seat with just ten weeks to prepare. This lack of preparation almost proved fatal.

For much of the flight, Carpenter suffered from an overheating pressure suit, with the biosensor registering 38.8°C at one stage. An experiment to observe a multicoloured balloon flopped when it failed to inflate.

More seriously, the over-enthusiastic astronaut consumed fuel at such a prodigious rate that he was obliged to let the craft tumble out of control as the third and final orbit began. Then he wasted further fuel chasing Glenn's fireflies.

A hurried preparation for re-entry ended in the capsule hitting the atmosphere several seconds late and pointing in the wrong direction. During final descent, the capsule's fuel tanks were totally exhausted, leaving it free to swing erratically from side to side. Carpenter's wild fairground ride was only ended by premature deployment of the drogue parachute.

Not surprisingly, Aurora 7 landed 250 miles (420 km) down range from the planned target area and out of touch with Cape communications. A frantic search operation finally ended an hour later when the capsule was spotted by an Air Rescue Service plane. Four hours passed before the exhausted astronaut set foot on the deck of the carrier Intrepid.

Carpenter's dramatic mission received public acclaim but internal opprobrium. Flight Director Chris Kraft was heard to exclaim, 'That sonofabitch will never fly for me again.' He had his way. Carpenter eventually turned to a different challenge, becoming an aquanaut in the Navy's 'Man-In-The-Sea' programme.

COSMONAUTS IN DISGRACE

At the time of Gagarin's breakthrough, a young, self-assertive pilot named Grigori Nelyubov was attracting a lot of favourable comment from the staff at Star Town. He had already acted as support crewman for the first flight, and had just been given a similar assignment for the forthcoming Vostok 3 when his career was dramatically terminated by a characteristic display of arrogance.

Nelyubov and two other cosmonaut recruits, Filatyev and Anikeyev, were involved in a drunken altercation with a military patrol at a railway station. When their identities were confirmed, the security officials offered to drop their charges if the group apologized. His two companions immediately agreed to this condition, but Nelyubov refused, so all three were reported for disciplinary measures.

General Kamanin was so furious when he read the incident report that he removed all three from the squad and sent them back to their Air Force units. Their colleagues blamed Nelyubov's intransigence for the episode and expressed deep regret at the loss of Filatyev and Anikeyev.

The disgraced Nelyubov tried unsuccessfully to convince his fellow pilots that he had been next in line for a Vostok mission. As he read about the dramatic successes of the Vostok and Voskhod crews, the emotional pressure told on his unstable temperament and he sought solace in drink. On 18 February 1966 the inebriated ex-cosmonaut stepped in front of a train near Vladivostok. Whether accidental or intentional, it was a sad end to a potentially brilliant career.

ADAM AND EVE IN SPACE

By the summer of 1962, both superpowers were under pressure to provide more space successes. Chief Designer Korolev was already looking ahead to docking two spacecraft in orbit, so what better way to create a sensation than by sending up two cosmonauts in separate ships? On 11 August 1962, Vostok 3 carried Andrian Nikolayev into orbit, followed the next day by Pavel Popovich in Vostok 4.

Western media hailed the 'first rendezvous on the road to the Moon', though the reality was rather different. Neither craft had the capability to change orbit or manoeuvre, so the cosmonauts simply sat back and watched entranced as the ships passed briefly within three miles (5 km) of each other.

Nikolayev made his mark on history by becoming the first man to make a live TV broadcast from space. He also ventured beyond the restraining influence of his couch, and reported that weightlessness was 'an amazingly pleasant state'. Both men were able to communicate and they even entertained each other by singing duets. Nikolayev parachuted to Earth after 94 hours in space. He was followed only six minutes later by Popovich, who had clocked up a 'mere' 70 hours.

In June 1963, it was Nikolayev's girlfriend who was grabbing the headlines. Twenty-six-year-old Valentina Tereshkova was a former textile worker with an impressive 126 parachute jumps under her belt. After their arrival at Star Town in March 1962, she and her four female colleagues underwent extensive pilot training as well as sessions in the centrifuge and isolation chambers before Tereshkova's assignment was confirmed in May 1963.

Apart from the female participant, there was little difference between the joint flight of Vostoks 5 and 6 and their predecessors. Indeed, the main justification for sending a relatively inexperienced woman into space was probably the demand from above for yet another exploit to impress the outside world. Unable to admit such a motive, Korolev spoke to the press about the need to learn more about human adaptation to weightlessness.

Valeri Bykovsky led the way in Vostok 5, to be followed 48 hours later by the first spacewoman. Her original programme called for a mission lasting one day, but she persuaded Korolev to allow her to extend her flight so that she could touch down at the same time as Bykovsky. The gritty young lady stood up well to bouts of sickness and disorientation, but suffered the indignity of a bruised nose as she parachuted back to Earth.

Vostok 6 remained in orbit for 71 hours, enabling Tereshkova to far outstrip the performance

Valentina Tereshkova, the first woman in space. (Theo Pirard–Tass)

of any of the Mercury astronauts. Her companion continued aloft for two more orbits, then returned to Earth after 81 orbits and nearly five days. Bykovsky's marathon remains the longest solo spaceflight to this day.

There was further cause for celebration in November when Andrian Nikolayev married the space heroine. Cynics suggested that the liaison was 'arranged' by the authorities in an attempt to discover more about the effects of radiation and weightlessness on the human reproductive system. If so, they received great reassurance when the world's first 'space baby', a girl named Yelena, was born on 8 June 1964. Thereafter, the couple slowly drifted apart, culminating in a divorce in 1983.

By the time Vostok 5 was sent aloft on 14 June 1963, Project Mercury was already completed. In October 1962, Wally Schirra demonstrated his piloting skills during a six-orbit, nine-hour engineering evaluation of the Mercury capsule. Determined not to fall into Carpenter's trap, the hard-nosed Korean War veteran spent much of the time drifting to conserve fuel. As Sigma 7 began re-entry, Schirra proudly announced that his fuel tanks were still more than two-thirds full. To cap it all, his craft splashed down only five miles (8 km) from the carrier *Kearsarge* in full view of its crew.

Last but not least, 'Gordo' Cooper was given the task of surviving one and a half days in orbit during May 1963. Far from being dismayed by the prospect of being confined in a tiny capsule more than 100 miles (160 km) above the Earth, Leroy Gordon Cooper Junior took the challenge in his stride.

Cooper's laid-back approach first surfaced when astonished ground controllers realized that the astronaut was contentedly dozing during countdown. In order to help the time pass more pleasantly, Cooper was given a more varied menu of cold dishes than his predecessors. Several experiments were also built into the flight plan, including the release of a small sphere with two flashing xenon lights. Cooper found Earth observation a delight, and sent back reports of streets, houses, trains and ships to sceptical ground controllers.

By the time Faith 7 completed her mission, she was hanging together by a thread. From the twenty-first orbit onwards, the automatic system was inoperative so Cooper had to re-enter using manual control. Despite the difficulty in firing the retro-rockets and holding the craft steady at just the right angle, Cooper succeeded in bringing his ship home just four miles (6 km) from the *Kearsarge*.

His extraordinary efforts brought the overall American manned spaceflight endurance to almost 54 hours, but this was a small fraction of the impressive total amassed by the Soviets. The astronauts, especially Alan Shepard, argued that a three-day follow-up mission was necessary, but the NASA authorities wouldn't wear it. They were already looking ahead to the next stage on the road to the Moon.

3

THE HEAVENLY TWINS

DESPERATE MEASURES

Nikita Khrushchev was becoming impatient. There had been no Soviet citizens in space since June 1963, and the Americans were preparing to launch their two-man Gemini spaceships. An equivalent Soviet craft was still several years away from making its maiden flight. Something had to be done, and quickly.

A flotilla of three Vostoks was rejected as an obvious publicity stunt, but a three-man crew had exciting propaganda value. In February 1964, Korolev approached one of his leading engineers, Konstantin Feoktistov, to suggest that he flew as part of such a crew.

By removing the ejection seat and forcing the crew to do without pressure suits, three men could be squeezed inside a modified Vostok capsule. This meant that there would be no escape system should there be a malfunction during launch. It also meant that the crew would have to land inside their spacecraft using a new soft-landing system which would operate just before it slammed into the ground.

Voskhod (Sunrise) also differed from its predecessor in having a solid fuel back-up retro-rocket. An alternative motor was needed since the craft would fly at a higher altitude than Vostok and its orbit would not automatically decay after ten days.

On 12 October 1964, the crew walked across the launch pad wearing only their sky-blue woollen suits and white communication helmets. Mission commander was 37-year-old Vladimir Komarov, a colonel in the Engineering Corps who had been grounded for a time because of an irregular heart beat.

Also on board were Feoktistov and Boris Yegorov, an Air Force doctor who specialized in aviation medicine. Both men had been given barely four months to train for the mission, a sign of the desperate rush to get the spacecraft off the ground.

Fortunately for all concerned, the mission went according to plan and their capsule touched down on the open steppe just over 24 hours after lift-off. However, as Korolev's successor, Vasili Mishin, recently admitted, 'The programme made no contribution whatsoever to the further development of space research. It was simply a waste of time.'

By the time the cosmonauts landed, Khrushchev had been ousted after a conspiracy within the Politbureau. It was the new power in the land, Leonid Brezhnev, who greeted the returning heroes at the traditional Moscow celebration.

With no other alternative available, Korolev was forced to consider a second Voskhod mission. This time he unveiled a collapsible airlock through which a cosmonaut would be able to leave his spaceship long before the first Gemini spacewalk.

The man chosen for the first walk in space was 30-year-old Lieutenant-Colonel Alexei Leonov. With him was Pavel Belyayev, a Second World War flyer who had overcome the setback of a badly broken ankle in August 1961. The airlock and the bulky pressure suits worn by the cosmonauts left no room for a third crew member.

A blizzard threatened the launch, but Voskhod 2 eventually took off from Baikonur on 18 March 1965, just five days before the first Gemini flight. The craft was placed into an elliptical orbit which carried it to a record apogee of 308 miles (495 km).

Belyayev helped his partner to strap the life support system onto his back before venting all the air in their cabin. Leonov then floated head first into the illuminated cylinder and waited for Belyayev to open the external hatch.

Peering over into the blackness of space, he slowly emerged, then turned and grasped the lip as the Earth flew by beneath him at nearly 18,000 mph (28,800 kmph). To record his achievement, he set up a cine-camera and flung the cover into the void. 'I'm pushing off!' came Leonov's voice. 'Don't rush it!' was Belyayev's anxious advice.

Uncertain of his movements, the cosmonaut opened his arms wide and floated away from the craft as far as the 17 foot (5 m) tether would allow. Pulling on the lifeline was the only way to gain some control over his movements, but even then an over-zealous tug sent him spiralling towards the spaceship. Fortunately, he managed to soften the blow with his hands.

After about ten minutes cavorting in space, it was time to call a halt. However, his spacesuit had ballooned outwards, causing any movements to be extremely tiring and making it virtually impossible to re-enter the airlock. Despite the risk of contracting the bends, he had no choice but to lower the pressure in his suit to a quarter of normal atmospheric pressure.

This did the trick, but he still had to struggle to unseat the cine-camera and push it into the tunnel before scrambling in head first behind it. He then had to turn himself round in the confined airlock so that he could enter the cabin feet first. The exhausted cosmonaut was perspiring profusely by the time he slid into his couch after 23 minutes 41 seconds outside.

His ordeal over, Leonov relaxed by sketching the wonders of the heavens in the ship's logbook. After jettisoning the airlock, Belyayev prepared Voskhod for automatic re-entry, but a failure in the orientation system postponed their homecoming. Ground control ordered an extra circuit to prepare for the first manually controlled re-entry by a Soviet spacecraft.

Retrofire took place on the eighteenth orbit, but the capsule was not aligned correctly and there followed one of the most hair-raising re-entries ever experienced. The heat around the capsule was so intense that its antennae fused, spreading liquefied metal over the porthole.

Voskhod 2 landed in the Ural Mountains, some 1,200 miles (2,000 km) from the intended landing site. At the Control Centre, there was near panic as no one knew their whereabouts or even whether they had survived.

Years passed before a truthful account of their ordeal was published. According to Yevgeni Riabchikov:

The parachute was caught in the treetops. The cosmonauts climbed out of their spacecraft. They made radio contact with the search party, giving their latitude and longitude. Then they built a campfire and pitched a tent. Soon hunters arrived on the scene, forest rangers made their way through the snow to them, and helicopters flew in. The helicopters dropped rope ladders, and doctors, cameramen and instructors climbed down. Campfires began to blaze merrily, and people started cutting down trees to make a landing pad for the helicopters.

Cosmonaut Georgi Grechko recently revealed further details:

They declared that the cosmonauts were having a rest in a sanatorium. Actually, they landed in deep snow among tall trees . . . They couldn't open the hatch and the fan inside the ship could not be cut off, making things even worse in that cold. Planes and helicopters dropped warm clothes but they got stuck in the tree branches.

Fortunately, the cosmonauts were fit enough to be flown to Moscow for a state reception. Leonov's spacewalk made him the prime Soviet candidate in the secret programme to land a man on the Moon. His partner was put in charge of training for the Moon programme but he died of peritonitis on 10 January 1970, the first spaceman to die of natural causes.

There were some proposals for a two-week Voskhod mission, and for a two-woman crew, one of whom would step out into space. It was even suggested that a Voskhod could be sent around the Moon, but this too was rejected. Two years would pass before the USSR launched another manned mission.

THE UNSINKABLE MOLLY BROWN

Apart from size, there were few obvious differences in external appearance between the Gemini and Mercury spacecraft. Gemini's maximum diameter of seven and a half feet (2.3 m) only resulted in a 50 per cent increase in cabin volume to accommodate twice as many crew. As astronaut Mike Collins wrote:

If you are five feet nine inches (175 cm), you can fully straighten your body; any taller and you will find your head banging the hatch or your feet bumping the floorboards, or both.

One significant modification was an offset centre of gravity in the Gemini which gave it a small amount of lift during re-entry. Packing all the heavy equipment into one side of the vehicle meant that pilots could now steer by rolling the spacecraft and pointing the lift vector in the appropriate direction.

Gus Grissom and rookie John Young were assigned to the Gemini 3 shakedown cruise on 23 March 1965. Grissom named their craft Molly Brown after the heroine of a Broadway play, *The Unsinkable Molly Brown*. This none too subtle reminder that Grissom's first craft lay on the bottom of the Atlantic did not go down well with the NASA hierarchy.

During a brief three orbits, the crew successfully changed their orbital plane and altitude. No one was taking any risks, so the track was lowered to ensure a safe re-entry even if the four solid fuel retro-rockets failed to fire. Inaccurate predictions of the amount of lift generated by the new design caused Molly Brown to hit the Atlantic 58 miles (93 km) off target.

More serious was the sudden jolt when the main parachute deployed. Both men were thrown forward, resulting in a smashed faceplate for Grissom and a badly scratched one for Young. Future crews were careful to raise a shielding forearm before releasing the huge canopy.

A WALK AROUND THE EARTH

NASA's original plans had not foreseen any astronaut walking in space until at least the third manned Gemini flight. This attitude changed after Leonov's sensational excursion. Engineers at Houston worked overtime to ready the pressure suit and other EVA equipment for the launch of Gemini 4, allowing NASA to add a spacewalk to the flight programme with just ten days to spare.

The second manned Gemini took off on 3 June, carrying James McDivitt and Edward

Ed White outside his Gemini spacecraft during the first American spacewalk. Note the hand-held manoeuvring unit. (NASA)

White. Catching up with their discarded Titan booster proved harder than anticipated, even though it lay only 600 feet (180 m) distant. The tumbling launch vehicle rapidly fell away until it was no more than a tiny object several miles below their line of flight. Further efforts to approach it also proved abortive, so in the end McDivitt and White abandoned the fruitless rendezvous attempts.

Preparations for the EVA began with a long checklist. Once they were satisfied, the cabin air was vented into space. As they approached Hawaii, White opened his hatch and fired the hand gun. The astronaut had a whale of a time somersaulting outside the capsule as McDivitt shot some spectacular footage. When the small unit ran out of gas, White tried pulling on his gold tether. After 23 exhilarating minutes, Mission Control issued the order to return to the haven of the capsule.

Curiously, as with Leonov's pioneering EVA three months earlier, the final stages proved to be the most hazardous. White's pulse zoomed up to 180 when his hatch refused to shut. Only after a combined attack, with McDivitt pulling on White's legs as White tugged from above, did the hatch finally give way, thus allowing the cabin to be repressurized.

During the remainder of the mission the crew worked diligently at their photographic and scientific assignments. Then, as home beckoned, their onboard computer let them down. Unable to obtain guidance control, McDivitt had to resort to a ballistic re-entry which generated 8g, twice the level experienced in an automatic re-entry. Gemini 4 splashed down 50 miles (80 km) short of the prime recovery ship, the USS *Wasp*.

Nevertheless, the mission had been so successful that Gordon Cooper and Charles 'Pete' Conrad were given the go-ahead for an eight-day cruise. Gemini 5 was the first to be equipped with fuel cells and rendezvous radar. Testing of the new equipment began only two hours into the flight when the crew ejected a Radar Evaluation Pod (REP) from the rear section. They successfully tracked it for the next 40 minutes until forced to shut down due to lack of power.

The problem lay with the new fuel cells. Within a few hours, oxygen pressure had fallen to one tenth of the normal level. Flight Director Chris Kraft decided to press ahead on a day-to-day basis. His decision was vindicated as the tank pressure gradually improved, and by the end of the week the astronauts had more power available than they could use.

Since further manoeuvres with the REP were out of the question, ground controllers gave the crew a 'phantom' target to chase. Within two orbits, the crew succeeded in arriving close to their intended position.

The early excitement gave way to a rather monotonous period of experiments, cold meals and exercises. The crew found sleeping alternate shifts a major headache, and strongly recommended that joint sleep sessions be scheduled in future. One unusual diversion came when they were able to speak to former astronaut Scott Carpenter as he worked in a submerged laboratory off the Californian coast.

After almost 191 hours in space, Gemini 5 splashed down about 100 miles (160 km) from the target area, a most unwelcome addition to their list of achievements. This shortfall was due to an error in the data supplied by ground control. However, doctors were delighted with their condition, even though they were tired and dehydrated. Another reason for celebration was the fact that the Vostok 5 record had been smashed.

LAUNCH ABORT

Gemini 6 was intended to be a short duration test of rendezvous techniques using the upper stage of an Atlas-Agena rocket. On 25 October 1965, Wally Schirra and Tom Stafford were calmly following their launch countdown when the Atlas-Agena took off from a nearby pad. A little over six minutes later, their mission was scrubbed as an explosion ripped the booster apart.

Frustrated programme managers came up with an ingenious substitute, a dual Gemini mission. On 4 December, Gemini 7 soared away from the Cape at the beginning of an uncomfortable two-week-long haul for Frank Borman and Jim Lovell.

Eight days later, after heroic efforts to renovate the scorched pad, countdown for Gemini 6 recommenced. Once more perched atop the Titan, Schirra and Stafford heard its engines spring to life, the clock started ticking, then silence. The engines shut down!

Schirra was suddenly faced with a life or death decision – to abort the mission by yanking on the

Gemini 7 as seen from Gemini 6. (NASA)

ejection ring between his legs, or to stay put and hope for the best. According to the manual, the clock only started when a plug was disconnected from the base of the Titan. If the rocket had pulled away from its restraining bolts, there woud be an almighty fireball as the fuel-packed rocket toppled onto the pad.

Despite the apparently overwhelming evidence for a launch abort, Schirra gritted his teeth and waited. His gamble paid off. The quiescent Titan remained serenely upright.

An inquiry discovered that the tail plug had been prematurely shaken loose, causing the computer to abort the launch. More significantly, a plastic dust cover was found inside a fuel line. Not only would this have prevented a successful December launch, but it would also have caused a quick end to the October mission even if the Agena had behaved perfectly!

Once again, the overworked ground staff rushed to recyle the countdown before time ran out. It proved to be third time lucky. On 15 December, Borman and Lovell were able to watch the trouble-free ascent of their companions from the Cape.

Gemini 6 arrived in orbit 1,380 miles (2,200 km) behind its stablemate. Schirra and Stafford obtained a firm radar lock with 230 miles (370 km) still separating them. Five hours and 50 minutes after take-off, Schirra pulled up just 120 feet (36 m) from the snub-nosed target.

For more than five hours, the two crews were able to speak and wave to each other as their craft pirouetted around the globe. Navy pilots Schirra and Stafford could not resist displaying a placard which read 'Beat Army'. Then the irrepressible Schirra startled Mission Control by sending a UFO report. 'We have an object, looks like a satellite, going from north to south, up in a polar orbit . . .' Loudspeakers reverberated to the sound of 'Jingle Bells' as Christmas came a little early to Houston that year.

Before the sleep period, Gemini 6 pulled away to a safe distance. Less than 26 hours after launch, Schirra and Stafford returned to Earth. Their craft hit the ocean only seven miles (11 km) off target, enabling the crew to be hoisted aboard the carrier *Wasp* inside their craft.

Once again in splendid isolation, Borman and Lovell wondered if they and their craft could endure three more days. To make life a little easier, they spent as much time as possible dressed only in their increasingly soiled underwear, surrounded by a growing pile of garbage.

Jammed into their seats 24 hours a day, there was no privacy and no opportunity for movement. For two weeks they shared a unique intimacy, comparable to prisoners locked inside a tiny cell.

As the days dragged by, they kept track by scratching the tally on the cabin wall. With its fuel cells slowly dying and a couple of thrusters performing nasty tricks, Gemini 7 limped into the home straight. Fortunately, splashdown was only six miles (9.5 km) from the *Wasp*, allowing its crew to witness their second spacecraft recovery in three days. This time the astronauts elected to be winched aboard a helicopter.

When the two grubby, bewhiskered space voyagers stepped onto the carrier's flight deck they were as pale as ghosts, exhausted and unsteady, but post-flight examinations showed they in relatively good shape.

Borman had lost ten pounds (4.5 kg) and Lovell six pounds (3 kg) in weight, mainly through dehydration. Both astronauts agreed that the lightweight suits and their freedom to disrobe played a significant part in improving their physical condition and their ability to complete the flight.

TUMBLING IN SPACE

For the next mission, Neil Armstrong and David Scott were given the task of demonstrating orbital docking. On 16 March 1966, an Atlas-Agena was successfully injected into orbit, followed 100 minutes later by Gemini 8.

Within six hours they were poised alongside the stage. Given the green light by Flight Controller Keith Kundel, Armstrong slowly edged the nose of his craft into docking position. Using his spacecraft's thrusters, the command pilot was able to swing the combined structure around through 90 degrees.

As half an hour of joint flight neared completion, the huge combination suddenly began to gyrate like some crazy fairground ride. Unaware of the cause, and out of range of all ground stations for advice, the crew assumed the Agena was to blame and shut off its control system. But the problem didn't go away, so they decided the

best way to quieten things down was to separate from the stage.

It was an error which nearly cost Armstrong and Scott their lives. The rate of spin increased rapidly until in a matter of minutes their craft was rotating once every second. Their pulses raced to 150 as all Armstrong's attempts to slow the accelerating motion met with failure. There was no alternative but to shut down the entire attitude control system and engage the automatic thrusters reserved for re-entry.

This drastic remedy brought the ship under control, but at the cost of their mission. Flight Director John Hodge ordered a hasty return to Earth. Ships and aircraft were rushed to an emergency landing zone in the Pacific Ocean about 500 miles (800 km) south-east of Japan.

Retrofire was successfully accomplished over central Africa, and 32 minutes later the capsule plopped into the rolling swell with a pinpoint splashdown. Their flight had lasted a little over 10½ hours.

The unhappy astronauts were picked up by the destroyer *Mason*, then endured an 18-hour cruise to Okinawa. Analysis of the crisis showed that a stuck yaw left thruster in the Gemini had been the culprit. A minor fault in some small, insignificant part of the multi-million-dollar hardware had almost brought about a disaster.

THE ANGRY ALLIGATOR

The Gemini 8 jinx seemed to transfer itself to the next in line. The first blow came on 28 February 1966 when the Gemini 9 prime crew of Elliott See and Charles Bassett died in a plane crash. For the first time, the back-up crew of Tom Stafford and Eugene Cernan had to step into the breach.

On 17 May, the Atlas-Agena again exploded soon after leaving the Cape. Conditioned by previous disappointments, NASA officials were ready with a replacement. On board was a small Augmented Target Docking Adapter (ATDA) equipped with all necessary navigational aids.

Two weeks later, Stafford and Cernan sat once more inside their capsule waiting for the all clear. This time, the Atlas seemed to have performed admirably, but ground control was unable to confirm whether the protective shroud

surrounding the ATDA had successfully separated.

A series of communication breakdowns forced a launch postponement, but on 3 June they eventually soared into orbit only to have their worst fears confirmed. The shroud over the ATDA was still in place. Stafford reported, 'Both the clam shells of the nose cone are still on but they are open wide. It looks like an angry alligator.'

Signals from the ground failed to shift the shroud so the disappointed crew had to be satisfied with an alternative programme of rendezvous manoeuvres around the ATDA. Later they moved to within three inches (7.5 cm) to snap detailed pictures of the wires which stubbornly held the 'jaws'. After their exertions, Mission Control agreed to postpone Cernan's spacewalk until the next day.

More than two hours of preparation were needed before America's second spacewalk. At last, as Gemini drifted into sunlight, cabin depressurization was completed. Standing on his seat, Cernan spent about 20 minutes retrieving a micro-meteorite package, deploying handrails and setting up a movie camera, then floated out through the hatch.

The 'Angry Alligator' showing the partly open shroud which prevented Gemini 9 from docking with the Augmented Target Docking Adapter. (NASA)

Taking care not to tangle himself in his 25 foot (7.5 m) long lifeline, he worked his way to the rear adapter section. With night fast approaching, he returned to the hatch area to change the film in the EVA camera and switch on the external lights. Back at the ship's stern, he attempted to put on a huge backpack called an Astronaut Manoeuvring Unit (AMU) which was stowed in the centre of the adapter.

Everything seemed more difficult than on the ground. Cernan began to overheat as he worked in semi-darkness, pulling down the AMU's arms, switching on its power supply, attempting to transfer his oxygen supply and voice link to the backpack and then strap himself in. Soon his pulse was racing at up to 180 beats per minute and he was perspiring so heavily that the suit's environmental system could not cope.

Faced with a fogged visor and garbled communications, the overworked astronaut took a break until sunrise. Even then there was little improvement, so it was decided to terminate his walk 45 minutes early.

Stafford helped his fatigued companion back inside, but the two men spent another 15 minutes wrestling with the umbilical before they were able to secure the hatch and repressurize their cabin.

Towards the end of their third day in orbit, Gemini 9 dropped into the Atlantic in full view of the *Wasp*. NASA Deputy Administrator Robert Seamans had to admit that there was still a lot to learn about docked operations and activities outside the spacecraft.

RIDING THE AGENA

For once, there were no hiccups with Gemini 10. Rendezvous with the Agena used more fuel than expected, but John Young was pleased with the smooth docking he achieved almost six hours after launch.

There followed a unique session of orbital billiards. Using the Agena main engine, the docked Gemini was blasted into a highly elliptical orbit which carried it a record breaking 475 miles (760 km) above the Earth.

Over the next two days, the linked hardware was gradually shifted into a 240 mile (380 km) circular path. There was a brief diversion while Michael Collins stuck his head out of the hatch to photograph the ultraviolet sky, but he was rudely interrupted when both men were afflicted by a sudden watering of the eyes. There was no choice but to close the hatch prematurely. As the problem slowly cleared, they decided some contaminant in the air filter must be to blame.

Their next task was to separate from the Agena and commence pursuit of its twin, abandoned months before by Armstrong and Scott. When the inert Agena 8 drifted into view, Collins' sextant-based calculations guided Young alongside with 15 per cent fuel remaining.

While Young concentrated on keeping the stage in the beam of his spotlight, Collins fought to don his chest pack and plug in a 50 foot (15 m) lifeline before venturing outside. Retrieving a small micrometeorite detection plate posed no problems, but both men were acutely aware of the danger from Gemini's 16 thrusters which could burn a hole in a spacewalker's suit.

Launch of Gemini 10 on 18 July 1966. This multiple exposure photograph shows the gantry being lowered prior to lift-off. (NASA)

After a struggle, Collins attached his hand 'gun' to its fuel supply in the body of the spacecraft. Pushing against the Gemini, he launched across the 10 foot (3 m) gulf which separated him from the Agena. Grasping its slippery docking adapter with both hands, he began to work his way around it but lost his grip and cartwheeled away into space. After describing a huge arc in the sky, he found himself gliding back alongside Gemini.

For the second attempt, Collins turned to his hand unit for propulsion. Careful to avoid a vicious-looking hook-shaped wire dangling from the Agena, he grabbed hold of some cables and gingerly moved around to the micrometeorite package which came free first time. Deciding it was too risky to install a replacement, he hauled himself along the umbilical back to the Gemini.

Two disappointments spoiled his successful

venture. The photographic record of his exploits was lost when his Hasselblad 70 mm camera somehow floated away into the void. Then they ran low on fuel, so Collins had no choice but to squeeze himself back into the cabin, then close the hatch.

Once some semblance of order was restored, they dumped overboard all unnecessary equipment. Most of their remaining fuel was used to lower Gemini's orbit, and retrofire took place about 70 hours into the flight, bringing the capsule down near the carrier *Guadalcanal*.

THE TIE THAT BINDS

After two scrubs due to technical hitches, Gemini 11 chased its Atlas-Agena heavenward on 12 September 1966. Astronauts Conrad and Gordon used a 'brute force' technique to bring them alongside the Agena for the fastest docking in space history – only 94 minutes after leaving the Cape.

Before the first rest period, both men practised undocking and docking with the Agena. The booster's engine checked out satisfactorily, so the way was clear for Dick Gordon's spacewalk the next day.

With Pete Conrad holding onto his feet, Gordon set up the EVA camera, deployed a handrail and retrieved an experiment package, but he was already feeling tired even before he began to swim unaided towards the attached Agena. His first attempt to attach a tether to its docking adapter ended in failure, so Conrad had to reel him in for a second try. With few hand or footholds, the operation proved far more difficult than expected, but Gordon persevered, legs astride the booster. Conrad yelled encouragement. 'Ride 'em cowboy!'

By the time the tether slipped into place, Gordon was partially blinded by perspiration, and his suit was overheating. Conrad sensibly saw no point in continuing and ordered him back inside. The excursion had lasted 33 minutes, one-third of the time allotted. An hour later, all excess baggage was unceremoniously dumped overboard.

Next day, Conrad and Gordon gained an unprecedented bird's-eye view of our planet as the Agena propelled them to a height of 850 miles (1,370 km). For two orbits the crew eagerly clicked their camera shutters to capture a portfolio of spectacular scenic panoramas.

Although they soon dropped back to a more normal altitude, the crew were able to take more pictures of Earth as well as a series of astronomical photographs during a two-hour stand-up EVA. Conrad actually dozed off during a lull in activity as they zipped across the Atlantic. When he awoke, he found his partner hanging on his tether, also fast asleep!

It was now time to undock and back away, slowly unravelling the tether which had tested Gordon's patience and stamina so much on his 'bronco ride'. Each time they rotated the Gemini, the line began to loop like a skipping rope but eventually the slowly rotating combination became very stable. Their instruments told them that they had become the first people to generate artificial gravity in orbit.

Cutting loose the Agena, they moved away to a safe distance. The last day of the mission was marked by one final approach to the target vehicle, then initiation of automatic re-entry as they passed over Canton Island. The capsule hit the water only 1½ miles (2.5 km) from the USS *Guam*, enabling them to be whisked aboard in a record-breaking 24 minutes.

A GRAND FINALE

The way was clear for James Lovell and Edwin 'Buzz' Aldrin to bring down the curtain on the Gemini programme. On launch day, each of them wore a placard bearing one word, 'The' and 'End'.

With an appropriate sense of occasion, both the Agena and the final Titan-Gemini combination sailed unerringly into orbit on 11 November. Aldrin had to resort to sextant readings after the first Gemini radar failure, but they successfully drew alongside the target 3 hours and 46 minutes after take-off. A routine docking took place half an hour later.

Unfortunately, Gemini's fuel cells were beginning to play up. Then a check-out of the Agena suggested that its primary engine was not to be trusted, so the crew had to make do with its

secondary thrusters to alter their orbit. These brought them into position for a seven-second skip through the Moon's shadow, just long enough to grab two snapshots of a fleeting solar eclipse.

The first day ended with a 2½-hour stand-up EVA. Aldrin installed a telescopic handrail and a movie camera, retrieved some experiments and snapped away at the blue Earth.

Another excursion next day proved highly successful as Aldrin took advantage of an improved system of tethers and restraints. The only problem during the entire session was when he failed to install a camera on Gemini's stern.

Subsequent tethered manoeuvres with the Agena were complicated by a couple of inoperative thrusters. The two craft eventually separated 52 hours 14 minutes into the flight. Aldrin's third EVA to dump their refuse overboard and take more photographs enabled the future Moon walker to establish a new overall record of 5 hours 32 minutes outside his spacecraft.

Minor problems with thrusters, fuel cells and water supply continued to dog them, but the last American two-man spacecraft hit the Atlantic close to the *Wasp*. Lovell joined his companion in the record books by chalking up 425 hours 10 minutes from his two Gemini voyages.

In little more than 18 months, the United States had logged well over 1,900 hours of space experience, a catalogue of successes which cleared the way for the giant leap to the Moon.

The Agena Target Docking Vehicle lingers close to Gemini 11. The tether which linked the two craft has just been released. (NASA)

Gemini splashdown. Frogmen attach a flotation collar to the spacecraft and assist the astronauts to disembark. (NASA)

4

THE ROCKY ROAD
TO THE MOON

THE BIRTH PANGS OF APOLLO

When President Kennedy committed the United States to a Moon landing, no one in his administration or even within NASA had any idea how to accomplish his dream. Most of the space agency's top people assumed that one section of a huge rocket sent from Earth would land on the Moon, then return directly to Earth. Von Braun already had plans to build a towering goliath known as Nova. However, detailed studies soon made it clear that such a mission would be incredibly difficult to achieve.

There were two other possibilities: assemble a massive Moon craft in Earth orbit from two separate sections, or detach a small, separate craft which could land on the surface and then return to dock with its mother ship. John Houbolt at NASA's Langley Centre championed this Lunar Orbit Rendezvous plan. Eventually he converted Bob Gilruth, Head of the Manned Spaceflight Centre at Houston, and NASA Administrator Jim Webb. From this decision sprang the Apollo programme with its Saturn V heavy-lift booster and two-spacecraft combination.

The cone-shaped Command Module (CM) would be home for three astronauts during the six-day cruise to and from the Moon. It measured 13 feet (4 m) in diameter across the heatshield and had a maximum height of 11 feet (3.3 m). Although far from spacious, it was large enough for three men to stand upright and float freely around the cabin.

Attached to the rear of the CM was a large Service Module (SM), which provided the essential power, oxygen, fuel and propulsion systems. This section would be jettisoned prior to re-entry.

While the CM needed an aerodynamic shape, a heatshield and a parachute system in order to descend safely through Earth's atmosphere, the Lunar Module (LM) could take on almost any shape. Grumman Aerospace designed a weird-looking craft composed of two sections. Its ascent stage would take off from the Moon using the lower descent stage as a launch platform. More than 70 per cent of its overall weight was taken up by fuel.

RIFTS BEHIND THE IRON CURTAIN

Sergei Korolev also foresaw the need to build a heavy-lift launch vehicle. Studies for such a rocket, later known as the N-1 (Nosityel or Carrier 1) began in May 1960. At the same time, the bureau of Vladimir Chelomei, which normally specialized in military programmes, started work on the Proton, a medium-lift rocket capable of sending a manned spacecraft around the Moon.

The debate about the best method to achieve a Moon landing was not resolved until 1964, when the Soviets decided to try for Lunar Orbit Rendezvous using the N-1.

Meanwhile, internal rivalries divided the rocket designers into two camps. Korolev's team argued strongly in favour of high energy propellants such as liquid hydrogen, liquid oxygen and kerosene for the new rocket, exactly the same combination to be used by the Saturn V.

Valentin Glushko, head of the most important engine manufacturing bureau in the country, insisted that toxic substances such as fluorine and nitric acid could reduce rocket size and weight.

Refusing to give way, Korolev turned to the aircraft engine firm led by Nikolai Kuznetsov. Lacking experience in building huge rocket motors, Kuznetsov decided to rely on a large number of medium thrust engines to power the N-1.

To carry 95 tons into Earth orbit, the N-1 would use a first stage propelled by no less than 30 separate motors, with another eight motors on the second stage and four on the third stage. The remainder of the rocket train which made up the 2,700 ton monster would consist of two more rocket stages, a lunar lander and a Soyuz for the return to Earth.

At the end of 1965, Korolev was given the go-ahead for a programme to send two cosmonauts around the Moon using Chelomei's Proton and his new Soyuz craft. Then came a shattering blow. Korolev finally succumbed to long-term heart trouble and the strain of overwork. The genius and inspiration behind the staggering Soviet space successes died on 14 January 1966. He was 59 years old.

His deputy and successor, Vasili Mishin, lacked the master's status and influential friends. He found it impossible to unify the work contracted out to 500 different organizations under the umbrellas of 26 separate ministries and departments.

Nevertheless, in November 1966, a project to land one cosmonaut on the Moon was put in hand. The ambitious plan called for the N-1 to begin flight tests in the autumn of the following year. Hopes were high that they might yet beat the Americans to the Moon.

A complex series of manoeuvres was planned for the Moon landing. The combined Soyuz-lander would brake into lunar orbit. One crewman would spacewalk from the Soyuz to the landing craft. Once the lander separated, its main propulsion unit would fire to slow it for descent. Its work completed, this engine would then separate to allow final adjustments by the lander's own motor. In this way, the cosmonaut's life would depend on the perfect operation of not one, but two different descent engines!

After four hours on the surface, the lander's ascent module would return to orbit and dock with the waiting Soyuz. The Soviet Moonwalker would then spacewalk back to the mother ship, the lander would be jettisoned, and a large propulsion unit on the Soyuz would send them on their way back to Earth. The heroes' return to their homeland would be completed in the Soyuz descent module.

'WE'VE GOT A FIRE IN THE COCKPIT!'

As 1966 dawned, NASA managers were in confident mood. Von Braun's Saturn IB passed its initial trials with flying colours, so there seemed every chance that a manned shakedown cruise of the Apollo Command Module would take place before the end of the year.

Prime crew for this milestone consisted of veterans Gus Grissom and Ed White, plus newcomer Roger Chaffee. Grissom's ship was an early version of the Command Module known as Block 1. Its main distinction was the absence of docking gear which meant that it was unable to link up with a Lunar Module. Block 2, the ultimate Mooncraft, was still far from operational.

NASA officials were in such a hurry to get Apollo off the ground that they readily accepted a badly flawed first Command Module. Between its delivery to NASA in August 1966 and the following January, spacecraft 012 was subjected to a remarkable 623 alterations.

An increasingly dissatisfied crew spent long hours trying to iron out the niggling technical hitches. Most serious of these was on 25 October when a Service Module fuel tank exploded. The launch date for Apollo 1 slipped ever further into 1967.

Then on 27 January, the crew clambered into their cabin far above the launch pad for their first full ground test. Before they began, Grissom requested that a simulated emergency evacuation be tacked onto the end of the session. Since the rocket was empty of fuel, no major hazards

*The Soviet lunar lander (left) never flew but a few
engineering models still exist and have recently been
revealed to Western visitors. Unlike the American Lunar
Module, it was designed to carry only one man to the
surface of the Moon for a brief period of exploration. The
conical structure on top of the spherical ascent stage appears
to be the attitude control system. The N-1 rocket (right)
was to have been used for the manned lunar flight, but it
was scrapped after four launch failures. (from drawings
by Ralph Gibbons)*

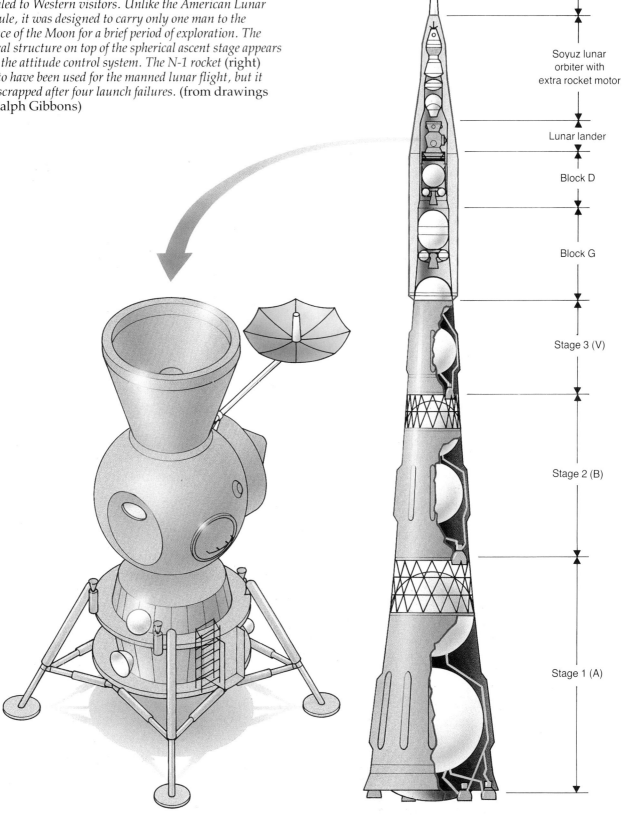

Escape tower

Soyuz lunar
orbiter with
extra rocket motor

Lunar lander

Block D

Block G

Stage 3 (V)

Stage 2 (B)

Stage 1 (A)

were contemplated so emergency services were on ordinary standby.

With the hatch sealed behind them, the cabin was pressurized to 16 psi of pure oxygen, higher than normal atmospheric pressure to prevent nitrogen leaking inside. Things went badly and there were numerous hold-ups, particularly involving poor communications. At one point an irritated Grissom exclaimed, 'How do you expect to get us to the Moon if you people can't even hook us up with a ground station? Get on with it out there.'

The five and a half hour marathon seemed to be approaching an end when the simulated countdown was put on hold at T − 10 minutes. Then at 6.31 pm, the evening calm was shattered by an almost casual report from Chaffee. 'Fire, I smell fire.' TV monitors showed how the astronauts sprang into action to initiate evacuation procedures. A more urgent cry for help came across the intercom. 'Fire! We've got a fire in the cockpit!'

For an instant no one reacted, then the grave danger facing the astronauts suddenly dawned and pad personnel began to scramble for the bolts which held Apollo's hatches in place.

It was too late. Only 16 seconds after the initial fire report, the intense heat ruptured the spacecraft cabin in a violent explosion. An outbreak of small fires and dense black smoke in the gantry further delayed rescue attempts.

About five minutes passed before the hatches were eventually removed. It was hard to recognize anything in the scorched interior, but eventually the fate of the three men was learned. Chaffee was still strapped into his couch.

Astronauts training for the Apollo 1 mission. Front to rear: *Roger B. Chaffee, Edward H. White II, James A. McDivitt. Chaffee and White perished in the Apollo 1 fire.* (NASA)

Grissom was stretched out seeking shelter beneath the centre seat. White's body lay below the hatch sill, a testimony to his frantic efforts to release the inner hatch. They were welded into position by a congealed mass of melted electrical insulation, Velcro and nylon.

All work on the programme ground to a halt as the post-mortem began. The official cause of death was asphyxiation after the explosion had damaged their protective suits. Although the exact reason for the fire was never established, there was strong evidence that an electrical short had ignited some combustible material and flames had spread uncontrollably in the pure oxygen environment.

Much more disturbing, inspectors reported bare wires, poor installation procedures, and lack of quality control in a spacecraft packed with inflammable materials. A close look at spacecraft 017 being assembled at Downey revealed no less than 1,407 flaws. Many of the design changes had not even been documented.

The inquiry board also demonstrated that Grissom had a right to be concerned over emergency evacuation procedures. With two hatches to remove before the crew could emerge – six bolts holding down the inward opening inner hatch could only be removed with a wrench – it was impossible to escape in less than 90 seconds.

Almost two years passed before everyone was satisfied with Apollo 1's replacement. No more Block 1 Command Modules were built. The Block 2 was given a new, outward opening hatch which could be opened from the interior within ten seconds. In future, pure oxygen was not to be used until the craft entered the vacuum of space. Inflammable materials were removed or replaced whenever possible, and future crews were to wear fire-resistant suits.

THE FATAL ROMAN CANDLE

Meanwhile, behind the usual veil of secrecy, Mishin and his cohorts were preparing the long-awaited Soyuz. The man chosen to test the new craft was 40-year-old Vladimir Komarov.

Early on 23 April 1967, he strolled across the launch pad wearing a blue nylon top, slacks and light shoes. At 3.35 am Moscow time, the night sky lit up as his Soyuz booster accelerated away from the gantry. Western commentators expected Komarov to be joined by a second craft within 24 hours for the first docking by two Soviet spacecraft.

Once injected into a near circular 130-mile (210 km) orbit, everything seemed to be going smoothly, although there were no TV transmissions and few details of in-flight manoeuvres. Reliable two-way radio links were established, and at the end of his fifth circuit, Komarov reported that the flight programme was being fulfilled successfully and he was feeling well.

As the craft drifted out of range of Soviet ground stations between 1.30 pm and 9.20 pm, Komarov was allowed a rest period. The next hard news came when Tass announced that Komarov had completed 13 revolutions and was in good health. Then came the sudden announcement that the mission had been completed and the cosmonaut was returning to Earth.

As he passed over Africa, Soviet news media announced a successful retrofire and separation of the spaceship's instrument module. But there was no triumphant broadcast to mark the hero's safe return. Instead, an ominous silence reigned over the airwaves.

Almost 12 suspenseful hours dragged by before Komarov's death was reported. It was not long before the cause of the tragedy was announced. When the descent module's main parachute opened at an altitude of nearly four and a half miles (7 km), its shroudlines became twisted, causing Soyuz 1 to plummet into the ground at great speed, killing its unfortunate occupant.

Yuri Gagarin, Komarov's back-up for the test flight, insisted that all went according to plan until the final moments, but Western observers had their doubts and rumours began to circulate.

Some years later, Soviet émigré Viktor Yevsikov claimed that Komarov was the victim of Kremlin pressure for a propaganda victory. He stated that none of the four unmanned Soyuz test flights had been flawless, with the craft suffering from burnt parachute lines, a damaged heatshield, and malfunctions in the temperature control system and automatic attitude control system.

It is now known that Soyuz 1 ran into difficulties almost as soon as it reached orbit. One of the solar wings, a new innovation on manned spacecraft, stubbornly refused to open out, depriving the craft of vital power. The craft began tumbling when its automatic attitude control system gave out, forcing Komarov to resort to the manual back-up system. This also gave him problems, and at one point, Komarov is quoted as exclaiming, 'Devil machine! Nothing I lay my hands on works!'

Mishin, overseeing his first manned mission, was forced to scrub the planned link-up with Soyuz 2 and try to bring back the unhappy cosmonaut. An attempt to initiate a night re-entry on the seventeenth orbit had to be abandoned when the overworked cosmonaut was unable to orientate the craft correctly for retrofire. Instructions were recycled for three hours later.

Although the Soyuz was no longer tumbling and Komarov had been able to align his craft, it was a little off course and slowly spinning as the plunge earthwards began. Its drogue parachute deployed on schedule, but the main chute became jammed. Realizing that his craft's rate of descent had hardly slowed, Komarov followed normal procedure and released a back-up parachute. Unfortunately, the lines of the two chutes became tangled, resulting in the fatal Roman candle.

The capsule hit the steppe with such force that its pressure hull split and Komarov's body was thrown onto the surrounding steppe. Its solid rocket motors, which normally cushioned the touchdown, exploded, setting fire to the craft.

Yuri Gagarin eventually began training to fly Soyuz 3, but within a year, he, too, was dead. On 27 March 1968, just two weeks after resuming flight duty, his two-seat MiG-15 trainer crashed and burst into flames after passing through another aircraft's slipstream. The nation mourned as a second space pioneer was buried in the Kremlin Wall.

THE APOLLO ROADSHOW GETS UNDERWAY

Although there were no manned flights between April 1967 and October 1968, both sides were working feverishly behind the scenes to get their respective programmes back on course.

Unmanned lunar orbiters imaged the Moon's surface for potential manned landing sites, while other craft were sent to touch down and discover the true nature of its surface. Further progress came in October 1967 with the first automatic docking between two spacecraft, Cosmos 186 and 188. A repeat performance was carried out by Cosmos 212 and Cosmos 213 in April of the following year.

The first Soviet attempt to send a Soyuz-type craft around the Moon failed, but in September 1968, Zond 5 achieved the desired trajectory. Eavesdropping experts in the West were startled to hear a cosmonaut's voice crackling over the airwaves, but it was only a tape-recording. Although turtles, insects, plants and seeds were the sole living things aboard, it seemed a clear sign that a man would soon follow. The mission ended with the unintentional splashdown of the descent module in the Indian Ocean after a navigation system failure.

In the United States, the Saturn V Moon rocket was coming on stream. During its first flight test on 9 November 1967, known as Apollo 4 (there was no Apollo 2 or 3), the previously

unflown first and second stages of the giant booster performed admirably. The Lunar Module also passed its first operational checkover in late January 1968. However, a second Saturn V trial on 4 April hit problems when the booster began to vibrate and some upper stage fuel lines ruptured.

Fortunately, there was time to correct these problems. The first manned Apollo mission called only for a Saturn IB to carry a Command Module into Earth orbit for an 11-day trial run.

A Soyuz capsule touches down in a cloud of dust as its retro-rockets fire just above the dry steppe. (CNES/ Intercosmos)

Assigned to this important but unspectacular cruise were veteran Wally Schirra, who had already announced his intention to retire after the flight, and two more recent recruits, Donn Eisele and Walter Cunningham.

On 11 October, Apollo 7 lifted off from Cape Kennedy, the last launch from Pad 34. The much modified CSM was injected into a 140–174 mile (228–285 km) orbit, still attached to the Saturn's second stage. Separation came nearly three hours after launch, paving the way for a series of rendezvous manoeuvres over the next few days. In the absence of an LM, the crew had to make do with a white target between the open shroud panels on the S-IVB second stage.

Ground controllers were delighted with the performance of the revamped craft. Unfortunately, the same could not be said for the crew. Schirra had the misfortune to catch a cold early in the mission. As he dived into the supply of

Apollo 7 commander Walter Schirra tries out the escape hatch on a mock-up of the Block 2 Apollo Command Module. This new design was introduced after the Apollo 1 fire. (NASA)

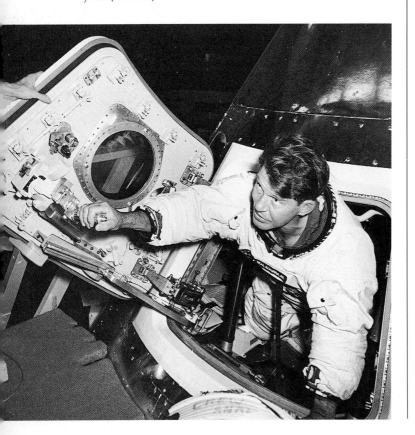

paper tissues and aspirins, his mood swung wildly between irritation and elation.

Schirra's cold put a damper on the scheduled TV transmissions as early as the second day. He angrily told controllers in Houston that the show was 'off'. When the men finally relented and switched on their camera for the first live television spectacular, they could be seen grinning broadly behind a placard which read, 'Keep those cards and letters coming in, folks.'

Unfortunately, as the cold virus spread through the crew, there was no let-up in the undeclared war between them and their opposite numbers on the ground. Their ultimate piece of insubordination was to refuse instructions to don their helmets during re-entry on the basis that their head colds might result in ruptured eardrums. Mission controllers reluctantly gave way, so the three rebels became the first astronauts to return to Earth holding their noses!

Swinging gently beneath a canopy of three huge parachutes, Apollo's maiden voyage ended in a choppy Atlantic. Secure on board the carrier *Essex*, a seasick Wally Schirra regained his sense of humour enough to appreciate a wisecrack about his 'first submarine service'.

IN THE BEGINNING, GOD CREATED THE HEAVEN AND THE EARTH

A few days after Apollo 7's splashdown, the unmanned Soyuz 2 was launched from Baikonur. The next day, 26 October, 47-year-old Georgi Beregovoi became the oldest space traveller when Soyuz 3 rose to meet it. Several times the two craft closed to within a few hundred feet of each other, but no docking was completed.

War hero Beregovoi continued in orbit for nearly two days after Soyuz 2 soft-landed in Soviet Central Asia. Although there was little to get excited about, the tests of the modified craft went smoothly. The Soviets were back in the race.

The pressures were on for NASA to take a shortcut to the Moon. With the Lunar Module still not available, there was a choice between a prolonged flight of the CSM in Earth orbit, or a highly dangerous swing around the far side of the Moon using the relatively untried Saturn V. Intelligence reports that the Soviets were ready to go for the first manned flight around the Moon settled the issue. Apollo 8 would head for the Moon.

In November Zond 6 repeated the lunar flyby of its predecessor, with the added bonus that it reduced its velocity by bouncing off Earth's upper atmosphere, a technique known as aero-braking. A controlled descent to the Soviet heartland took place after the second re-entry manoeuvre. All seemed set for a cosmonaut to take his seat for a half-million mile (800,000 km) trip around the Moon. But the December launch window, two weeks earlier than the Apollo 8 opportunity, passed quietly.

Cosmonauts Leonov and Makarov were ready to go. They had been training for just such a mission since February 1967. But after an accident involving the Proton booster, Mishin and his colleagues feared a repeat of the Soyuz 1 tragedy. The launch was scrubbed.

Two weeks later, Frank Borman, James Lovell and Bill Anders climbed aboard Apollo 8 for a perfect early morning launch. Gulping down fuel at a rate of 15 tons a second, the Saturn V slowly crept past the tower and accelerated out over the Atlantic. Eleven minutes 25 seconds later, Lovell reported engine cut-off a little more than 100 miles (160 km) above the Earth.

For the next two orbits, the crew and ground control gave the craft a rigorous checkout. Then came the critical moment when Apollo 8 was given a 'go' for translunar injection, the first time men had ever attempted to venture beyond Earth orbit. For just over five minutes the third stage motor fired to increase their speed to around 24,400 mph (39,000 kmph) – escape velocity – then it separated and gradually fell behind. Their path was so accurate that only one minor course adjustment was required during the next three days.

With Apollo in a slow 'barbecue roll' to ensure even heating of the spacecraft, the crew settled down for a long cruise, but Frank Borman upset the calm by becoming violently sick and fever-ish. NASA physician Charles Berry prescribed

rest and plenty of fluids, and the problem soon went away.

Half-way to the Moon, the astronauts put on a TV show displaying Earth as a small blur on the screens. By the time of their next broadcast, Apollo was 195,000 miles (310,000 km) from home, and had slowed to a snail-like 2,200 mph (3,500 kmph). A few hours later they began accelerating once more as lunar gravity took over.

The crew of Apollo 8 watch Earth appear above the lunar horizon. (NASA)

As they prepared to pass out of radio contact behind the Moon, Houston heard Anders say, 'Thanks a lot, troops. We'll see you on the other side.' The next half an hour was not suitable for anyone of a nervous disposition, but the main engine fired perfectly to place Apollo into an elliptical path around the Moon. Thirty-five minutes after loss of signal, a relieved ground control picked up Borman's voice. Another burn on the third lunar pass circularized the orbit at about 70 miles (110 km) above the surface.

On Earth, TV viewers preparing for Christmas Day were treated to a breathtaking view. As the myriad craters, large and small, drifted across their screens, the astronauts attempted a guided tour. 'The colour of the Moon looks like a very whitish grey, like dirty beach sand.'

On the ninth and penultimate lunar circuit, the crew tried to describe their feelings so far from home. Lovell came closest to hitting the mark. 'The Earth from here is a grand oasis in the vastness of space.' They concluded by reading from the Book of Genesis, 'In the beginning, God created the heaven and the earth . . .'

A 203-second blast from the main motor kicked Apollo out of lunar orbit and on course for home. The return journey proved uneventful apart from two more TV broadcasts which provided spectacular shots of a rapidly growing Earth.

As their speed increased to almost 25,000 mph (39,000 kmph) it was imperative that they hit the atmosphere at just the right angle. The Service Module was cast off and the Command Module turned round so that its blunt end faced forward. The capsule dipped into the upper atmosphere, then rose again before beginning its second and final plunge towards the ocean. Its drogue parachutes deployed on schedule at 34,000 feet (10 km), followed by the three main chutes at 10,000 feet (3 km). Apollo hit the water at a mere 17 mph (27 kmph).

Almost immediately, a helicopter from the *Yorktown* was hovering overhead, dropping flares. After a short but uncomfortable wait for daylight, the men were lifted aboard a chopper using a special 'Billy Pugh net'. Borman took the opportunity to shave, but his colleagues stepped out onto the carrier's deck proudly sporting their six-day growth.

THE FIRST ORBITAL UNION

Towards the end of 1968, there were signs of confusion and crisis in the Soviet camp. The cosmonaut group which had been training for the circumlunar trip was broken up soon after the triumph of Apollo 8, though Leonov was still a prime candidate for a lunar landing attempt some time in 1970 or 1971.

Then, in mid-January 1969, came evidence of a revival in the manned programme when Vladimir Shatalov took off on board Soyuz 4. All became clear the next morning when Soyuz 5 rose to meet its stablemate. On board were two members of the original cosmonaut corps, Boris Volynov and Yevgeni Khrunov, together with Alexei Yeliseyev, a spacecraft designer who had been recruited as recently as 1966. Khrunov had acted as back-up for Leonov's pioneering spacewalk four years earlier.

Using manual control, the trio closed on Shatalov until they lay only a few miles apart, then they took a breather while the spacecraft radar fed information to the onboard computers, enabling an automatic approach to within 300 feet (90 m).

Shatalov then resumed control and edged his ship towards the 'passive' Soyuz 5. Soyuz 4's coupling rod smoothly entered its partner's adapter cone. For the first time in history, two manned spacecraft were held firmly in each other's embrace – the Command Module–Lunar Module docking set for Apollo 9 was still seven weeks away.

More was to follow. Volynov helped his companions to don their pressure suits, complete with small life-support packs strapped to their legs. Once satisfied that all was airtight, he floated back into the Command Module and sealed himself inside.

Khrunov was the first to exit. He moved gingerly along the ship's hull, closely followed by Yeliseyev. Once inside the Soyuz 4 orbital module, they cut in the air supply, and with normal pressure resumed, helped each other to remove their suits. The entire episode had taken just one hour.

Shatalov was delighted to greet his two visitors, especially since they had brought him mail, newspapers and photographs from home. The

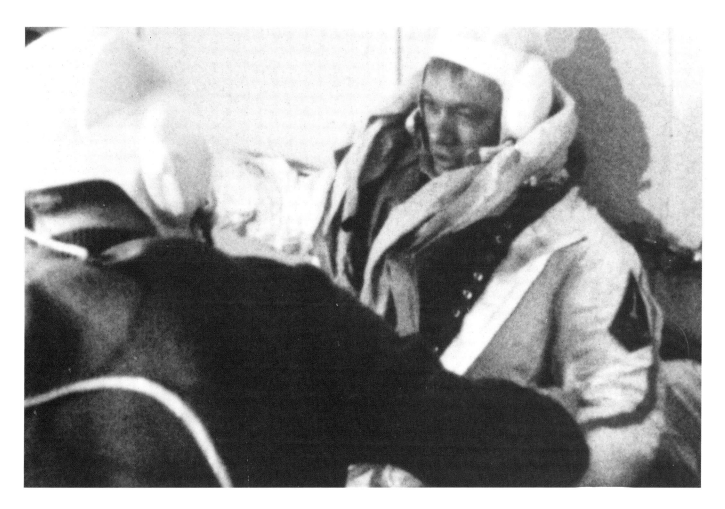

two spacewalkers settled down to sleep in the orbital compartment while Shatalov retreated to his contour couch in the Command Module. The next day, 17 January, both ships separated and returned to Earth.

The true significance of the dual spacewalk was not immediately apparent. We now know that this relatively primitive method of crew transfer would be needed for the proposed lunar landing. However, the Soviet heavy-lift booster had still not flown. Mishin and Kuznetsov tried to cut corners. Instead of spending time and money building a test-bed for their brainchild, they aimed for an all-out trial run.

On 21 February 1969, the N-1 was rolled out to the launch pad. At first, everything seemed to be going according to plan. The massive booster cleared the tower and headed out across the barren steppe, but, unknown to the onlookers, a fire had broken out in the tail section. Seventy seconds after lift-off, sensors detected the danger and switched off the engines, causing the rocket to plunge back to Earth.

SPIDER MEETS GUMDROP

While US spy satellites kept a close eye on developments at Baikonur, NASA prepared to get the Lunar Module operational. Jim McDivitt, David Scott and Rusty Schweickart had been waiting for their opportunity to fly since December 1966. Their wait was extended a little longer when they were grounded with head colds, but on 3 March, they clambered into Gumdrop, their irreverently named Command Module.

Almost immediately after they entered orbit, Scott fired the explosive bolts to free the CSM from the booster's third stage, then watched as the Lunar Module, Spider, shed its protective shroud. Turning his ship around to face back the way it had come, he edged towards the 'lunar bug' which nestled inside the cylindrical stage.

With the CM probe inserted into its housing on Spider, both craft backed out and pulled clear.

The next two days saw a series of stability tests during which the maximum altitude of the combination was raised to 300 miles (500 km). Despite attacks of space sickness, the crew opened up the docking tunnel between the two craft, checked out Spider and completed the first successful firing of its descent engine.

Schweickart's two-hour EVA to test the lunar pressure suit and its portable backpack was postponed due to his poor medical condition. When it did take place next day, he was restricted to a 40-minute series of checks while perched on the 'front porch' of the LM. A planned transfer between craft was cancelled, though Dave Scott briefly stuck his head out of the Command Module hatch.

The fifth day saw the first free flight by a Lunar Module. Wearing their pressure suits, McDivitt and Schweickart floated into Spider, moved to their standing positions, powered up its systems, and prepared to separate.

Suddenly, they were flying free. They backed away to a safe distance and rotated their craft so that Scott could check whether all four legs had unfolded. Given the all clear, the duo fired Spider's main engine to manoeuvre into a safe orbit which brought the two craft within rescue distance twice during each circuit.

The next step was to jettison their descent stage and fire the ascent stage engine for the first time to widen the gap to more than 100 miles (160 km). They were now out of visual contact and relying on instruments to find each other again. Once in a lower, faster orbit, Spider gradually closed on Gumdrop, pausing only for a mutual photographic session with 100 feet (30 m) between them. Soon after, the two ships were securely docked once more.

With his companions safely back inside the CM, Scott was able to discard Spider's ascent stage. During the remaining five days the crew kept themselves occupied by snapping away at Earth's surface, and conducting further trials of the CSM main engine. Bad weather in the

Russell Schweickart stands on the porch of the first Lunar Module, Spider. (NASA)

landing zone forced them to fly an extra orbit so that they could aim for a calmer part of the Atlantic. In a perfect finale, Apollo 9 eventually splashed down within three miles (5 km) of the carrier *Guadalcanal*.

THE FINAL DRESS REHEARSAL

There was a strong temptation to go straight for a lunar landing, but caution prevailed. Apollo 10 carried Tom Stafford, John Young and Gene Cernan, an experienced crew with plenty of rendezvous and docking practice under their belts. Blast off from Pad 39B came on 18 May.

As they passed over Australia on their second circuit, the third stage engine kicked them towards the distant Moon. Safely on their way, Young swapped couches with Stafford to separate CSM Charlie Brown from the third stage, turn a half-somersault through 180 degrees, close in and dock with LM Snoopy, then finally withdraw the 14-ton lunar lander.

Viewers on Earth were able to enjoy the first colour TV pictures from space during the three-day outward journey. The Service Module engine slowed their speed to 3,600 mph (5,760 kmph) so that they could slip into lunar orbit.

From an altitude of 69 miles (110 km), the battered landscape of Earth's nearest neighbour zipped past their window. The excited crew struggled for words to describe the grey-white plains, white-rimmed craters, and deep, sharp-sided channels.

22 May began with the first real problems of the mission. Loose insulation in the docking tunnel between the two craft entered Snoopy and blocked a vent used to alter cabin pressure. The crew had to use wet towels to mop up the mess. Then ground control warned them that Snoopy had slipped a few degrees out of alignment. Any further slippage might damage the docking latches and prevent its crew from linking up with the mother craft after their free flight.

With this warning ringing in their ears, the crew disappeared behind the Moon and out of radio contact. There were widespread sighs of relief when the two separate spacecraft reappeared flying in formation just 50 feet (15 m) apart.

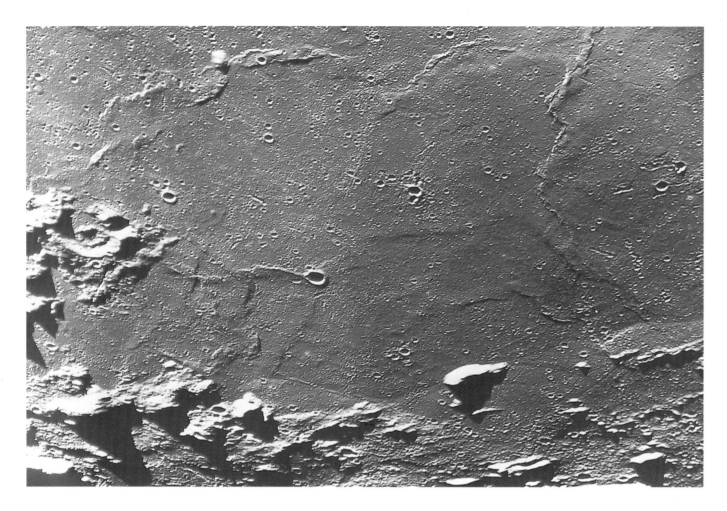

Apollo 10 photographed a number of possible lunar landing sites. This is Landing Site 3 in the Central Bay region. (NASA)

Stafford and Cernan fired Snoopy's descent engine to brake the flimsy module and send it swooping down towards the awe-inspiring terrain below. John Young was left alone in Charlie Brown, praying that he would not be called upon to attempt a rescue.

During the next hour, Snoopy swept to within nine miles (14 km) of the surface. Their radar system fed back accurate altitude data, though communications breakdowns proved a frustrating and potentially dangerous hazard.

After two grazing passes of the Moon's near side, it was time to seek out Charlie Brown, but when they first tried to jettison the redundant descent stage, it refused to budge. Then it suddenly shot off, leaving the startled astronauts inside a wildly gyrating ascent stage.

Within seconds, Stafford calmly took control and stabilized Snoopy. It turned out that the rough ride was caused by a switch being left in the wrong position, a checklist error freely admitted by ground control. Nevertheless, it was a relief when Snoopy's engine fired perfectly for the return trip to John Young in the CSM. 'Man, I'm glad I'm getting out,' was Cernan's comment after eight hours of independent flight.

With the docking tunnel closed up, Snoopy was cast adrift into an eternal orbit around the Sun. The remainder of the mission was fairly uneventful, and the main engine burn on the far side of the Moon brought Charlie Brown 'right down the fairway' on its homeward leg. The crew prepared for their homecoming by being the first to shave in weightlessness. Splashdown took place in the central Pacific eight days and three minutes after lift-off from the Cape.

American confidence was riding high. In the Houston control centre, a large sign appeared which read, '51 days to launch', a reference to the long-awaited expedition by Apollo 11 to another world.

5

MEN ON THE MOON

ONE GIANT LEAP

Although the Moon race was almost over, the Soviets were not yet ready to throw in the towel. The second trial of the N-1 took place only two weeks before the launch of Apollo 11. Once again it was a disastrous flop. The entire launch pad was devastated as the rocket exploded on ignition.

There was still one more card to play. On 13 July, the unmanned Luna 15 set off in an attempt to bring some Moon dust back to Earth. Worried NASA officials contacted the Soviets and were assured that it posed no threat. The road was clear for humans to set foot on another world.

The men entrusted with this monumental task were civilian Neil Armstrong, a former X-15 rocket plane test pilot, and Air Force Colonel Edwin 'Buzz' Aldrin. The third crewman, Air Force Lieutenant-Colonel Michael Collins, was particularly fortunate to be on board. He had been grounded by a loose disc in his neck which was pressing on his spinal cord. He was only passed fit after delicate surgery during the summer of 1968.

Moon fever struck as a million spectators, 3,000 press and 600 million TV viewers watched the final preparations with bated breath. At 9.32 am local time on 16 July, orange flame and billowing clouds of smoke belched from the mighty Saturn V as it gradually rose into a clear blue sky. Two hours 44 minutes after launch, Apollo 11 soared out of Earth orbit and, shortly after, Collins swung Columbia around to extract the LM Eagle from its space 'garage' inside the third stage.

During the next three days, the crew checked out their new home and broadcast several lighthearted TV shows. Finally, at 75 hours 41 minutes into the mission, Apollo 11 disappeared behind the Moon and braked into an elliptical lunar orbit.

Two hours later, the engine fired once more to circularize their path. Roused in the early hours of Sunday 20 July, they ate their last communal breakfast, then buried themselves in final preparations. Armstrong and Aldrin donned their pressure suits and began powering up the LM. Soon it was time to lower Eagle's legs and depart. Armstrong reported, 'The Eagle has wings!'

For the next 80 minutes all systems were checked, then Eagle's descent engine sent them swooping to within 10 miles (16 km) of the surface. Apart from some communications break-up, their bird was in beautiful flying fettle.

Strapped firmly upright for the 12-minute glide to the Sea of Tranquillity, Armstrong kept his eyes glued to the instruments while Aldrin read off the altitude and velocity. Several alarms warned of computer overload, but, quickly reassured by Houston, the men pressed on.

Suspense heightened as Armstrong lifted Eagle over a looming crater, but at last came the words everyone had been longing for: 'Contact light! OK. Engine stop.' Armstrong gave the world the glorious news. 'Tranquillity Base here. The Eagle has landed.' They had made it with just 20 seconds of fuel to spare.

First priority was to make sure everything was still shipshape, but ten minutes after touch-down, they were able to relax and admire scenery that was literally out of this world. Mission Control agreed to their request to proceed immediately with their first excursion. They eagerly began to put on their multi-layered EVA suits, plastic overboots, gloves, bubble helmets and portable life support systems, an extra 32 lb (14.5 kg) in the weak lunar gravity.

About six and a half hours after landing, Armstrong backed slowly out onto the porch and down the ladder, guided by the watching Aldrin. Half-way down, he pulled a lanyard to deploy their stowed equipment and a small TV camera. The largest television audience in history watched spellbound as Armstrong's ghostly grey image slowly jumped off the bottom rung. Then came the legendary words, 'That's one small step for man, one giant leap for mankind.'

The commander gingerly probed the powdery surface, leaving clear footprints in the dust. He then moved away a short distance to collect a contingency soil sample in case they had to beat a hasty retreat.

Fifteen minutes later, it was Aldrin's turn to leave the cabin, 'making sure not to lock it on my way out'. Once they discovered the best way to move around, they set up the scientific experiments, then hopped back to Eagle to unveil a plaque which read, 'Here men from the planet Earth first set foot upon the Moon, July 1969.'

Raising the Stars and Stripes was a struggle, but eventually the men stood proudly in front of their flag. Right on cue, Houston informed the astronauts that President Nixon wished to speak to them. As the President commented, 'This certainly has to be the most historic telephone call ever made.'

The ceremonies over, the men began collecting soil and rock samples. Armstrong used a special scoop to collect specimens while Aldrin attempted to hammer core tubes into the rigid ground. Once the precious samples were loaded onto Eagle with the aid of a pulley system, they climbed back aboard Eagle and closed the hatch after 2 hours 31 minutes outside the spacecraft. The grubby astronauts were able to cut into Eagle's oxygen supply, then dump overboard their used backpacks along with empty food containers and urine bags.

Armstrong rigged himself a hammock while Aldrin curled up on the floor, but the men slept fitfully. Next day, having completed 21 hours on the surface, Eagle's ascent stage blasted off, flattening the American flag they had so proudly installed.

Edwin 'Buzz' Aldrin backs down the ladder, ready to set foot on the Sea of Tranquillity. (NASA)

The Apollo 11 astronauts speak to President Nixon from inside the mobile quarantine facility after their epic voyage. Left to right: Neil Armstrong, Michael Collins, Edwin Aldrin, President Nixon. (NASA)

Collins watched the Lunar Module grow rapidly from a tiny speck until it was once again flying alongside Columbia. Docking on the far side of the Moon was nearly upset by an errant thruster, but Collins stayed in control. He greeted his friends with a warm bearhug, then it was down to the serious business of unloading their treasure. They completed their task so quickly that Eagle was jettisoned ahead of schedule.

On 22 July, a two and a half minute burn by the Service Module boosted them to escape velocity. They were on their way home. On their second TV broadcast, they shared some of their feelings with the watching multitudes and took the opportunity to thank everyone who had made their achievement possible.

The only hitch on the homeward leg came when gales forced the landing site to be moved 250 miles (400 km) downrange. As the eighth and final day dawned, it was a dirty, smelly crew and spacecraft which prepared for re-entry, despite a last minute shave.

With less than one hour to go before re-entry, the Service Module was discarded, exposing the Command Module's heatshield. Piercing the atmosphere at more than 27,000 mph (43,000 kmph), their body weight increased more than six times while the outside temperature reached nearly 3,000°C.

Radio contact was quickly established, and they parachuted to a perfect splashdown about 950 miles (1,500 km) south-west of Hawaii. Columbia turned turtle in the water, but it was soon righted by the flotation bags. Their ordeal was not yet over, however. Frogmen threw them special isolation garments, then they were sprayed with disinfectant and scrubbed each other down with an iodine solution. Their capsule was also decontaminated and sealed in case it carried any Moon bugs.

On board the *Hornet*, they went straight to a specially converted trailer known as the 'mobile quarantine facility', remaining there until they reached the lunar receiving laboratory in Houston.

Not until 10 August were the three intrepid explorers released to their families and a whirl-wind programme of engagements, parades and press briefings, followed by a 45-day world tour aboard Air Force One. None of them ever really became accustomed to the universal acclaim, and all three soon left NASA in search of another identity and new challenges.

THE NOT-SO-MAGNIFICENT SEVEN

Rather than admit defeat, the Soviets continued with their lunar programme. Although Luna 15 crashed into the Moon shortly before Eagle's departure, further unmanned craft soon followed.

Zond 7 looped behind the Moon in August 1969. Once again, a double skip through the upper atmosphere was employed to reduce its velocity during re-entry. Two more Luna robot samplers failed in September and October, but sandwiched between these flops was a space spectacular which involved three separate craft and seven men in orbit simultaneously for the first time.

Soyuz 6 was crewed by Valeri Kubasov and Georgi Shonin, a cosmonaut since 1959 but only now making his first trip into space. Soyuz 7 blasted off from Baikonur a day later, carrying Anatoli Filipchenko, civilian flight engineer Vladislav Volkov, and research engineer Viktor Gorbatko. After another 24-hour interval, the third Soyuz followed hard on their trail, occupied by the most experienced of the crews, Vladimir Shatalov and Alexei Yeliseyev. Rumours were rife that Soyuz 7 and 8 would soon repeat their predecessors' docking. A Soviet magazine even published a drawing of two such craft linked nose to nose. We now know that Soyuz 7 and 8 were indeed intended to link up, while the crew of Soyuz 6 were to film the entire operation. Everything seemed to be going well as the three craft approached to within a few miles of each other. On one occasion, Soyuz 7 and 8 lay only 1,600 feet (500 m) apart, close enough to 'wave their solar panels at each other', but there was no link-up. It is now known that the operation was cancelled due to a failure in the radio location system.

Soyuz 6 eventually dropped far behind its companions. Its crew retreated to the descent module, then depressurized the orbital module to try out three methods of automatic welding, watched by the flight engineer on a TV screen. Their five-day flight ended with a routine landing on the steppe north-west of Karaganda, followed by the other Soyuz craft on 17 and 18 October.

THREE SURVEYORS ON THE MOON

The second Moon landing was entrusted to an all-Navy crew commanded by 'Pete' Conrad. Alan Bean was assigned as pilot of the Lunar Module Intrepid while Richard Gordon was responsible for the Command Module Yankee Clipper.

On launch day, 14 November 1969, Cape Kennedy was threatened by a rapidly advancing storm, with the pad hardly visible from the viewing gallery. It was touch and go whether to scrub the launch, but the presence of President Nixon tilted the balance.

The Saturn V had barely cleared the tower when it was struck by lightning, followed almost immediately by a second strike. Alarm lights flashed on all over the console, bringing an urgent report from Conrad, 'We just had everything in the world drop out.'

A massive power surge shut down vital systems, but fortunately the rocket's guidance was unaffected, and the back-up batteries did their job. As they headed out over the Atlantic, the crew set about restoring order. Staging occurred right on schedule, and normal operations were resumed when the Command Module guidance platform was realigned once they were safely in orbit.

Apollo 12 was given the go-ahead to depart for the Moon on its second revolution and TV viewers were able to watch the successful docking with Intrepid and separation from the third stage.

After 22 hours on the hop, the crew spent most of their second day catching up on some sleep. Then came a mid-course correction which caused the craft to deviate from the safe, free-return trajectory.

Apollo 12 disappeared behind the Moon late on 17 November to complete a perfect braking manoeuvre into lunar orbit. Next day, Intrepid pulled away from the mother ship and, with the aid of Bean and the onboard computer, Conrad guided his craft 'right down the middle of the road' for man's second landing on another world. It was 1.54 am Cape time on 19 November 1969.

Four and a half hours after touchdown the 5 foot 6½ inch (1.68 m) Conrad jumped off the ladder with a quip, 'That may have been a small one for Neil, but that's a long one for me.' One happy astronaut bounded around collecting the contingency sample. He was soon joined by his colleague, but, unfortunately, a colour TV broadcast had to be abandoned when Bean burnt out the camera after pointing it at the brilliant Sun. Deployment of their new scientific package also proved rather frustrating as fine dust covered them from head to foot and minor problems kept arising.

With everything at last safely installed, they took a stroll to nearby Shelf crater. On the way they came across two unusual mounds, about four feet (1.2 m) high and five feet (1.5 m) across the top. Back at Intrepid, they found it much easier to sink a soil core tube than their predecessors. With plenty of oxygen remaining,

Alan Bean examines Surveyor 3, which landed in the Ocean of Storms in April 1967. The robot craft had returned more than 6,300 pictures before it expired. (NASA)

Conrad eventually closed the hatch 3 hours 56 minutes after he first ventured forth.

Mission Control gave them the green light for a second excursion the next day. They walked almost a mile around three sizeable craters, studying the local geology and picking up specimens. Each crater differed in appearance, though particles of glass were common on their rims or floors. Bending over was quite tiring, so Bean made life easier by grabbing hold of a strap on Conrad's backpack and steadying him as he leaned forward.

On the final leg, they examined Surveyor 3, the robot spacecraft which had set down there 31 months earlier. Although the craft had acquired a coating of brownish dust, it seemed in good condition. They snipped off some pieces from the craft for examination back on Earth.

Their second EVA brought total time on the surface to 7 hours 45 minutes, during which they collected 75 lb (34 kg) of rocks, plus 15 lb (7 kg) of Surveyor hardware. Unfortunately, they threw away the colour shots of Surveyor among the rubbish, so only the black and

white views have been passed down for posterity.

Intrepid departed from the Moon 31½ hours after touchdown. Determined to keep a clean ship, Gordon forced his comrades to disrobe and float naked through the tunnel. Fortunately, the scene was not recorded for the millions of TV viewers back home!

When Intrepid was set free and sent plunging into the lunar surface, scientists were amazed to see the seismometer 'ringing' for over 40 minutes – far longer than expected.

Their final day in lunar orbit was spent continuing the detailed orbital survey begun by Gordon, including a search for future potential landing sites. On 21 November, they set off for home.

The highlight of the return leg came when Earth moved in front of the Sun, leaving our planet encircled by a blue corona. Two minor course corrections put Yankee Clipper right on target for her Pacific splashdown, and their trip ended in rough seas only three miles (6.5 km) from the *Hornet*.

Although they were spared the full isolation routine, they still had to wear germ-filtering face masks and were hustled straight into the mobile quarantine unit. They remained out of touch with their families and friends for another 16 days before emerging to universal acclaim.

'WE'VE HAD A PROBLEM'

Within a few months of Apollo 12's triumph, three of the eight scheduled Moon landing missions had been cancelled. Public enthusiasm for the multi-billion-dollar programme was waning and the Nixon Administration wanted to sustain the war in Vietnam while trimming the domestic budget.

As morale among NASA employees and contractors plummeted, preparations for Apollo 13 were hit by a series of unusual glitches. In particular, one of the Service Module tanks refused to vent oxygen properly and had to be emptied by using its internal heater.

The crew was also affected. Back-up LM pilot Charles Duke contracted German measles, a disease for which CM pilot Thomas Mattingly had no immunity. Mattingly was replaced by Jack Swigert, who only had a few days to prepare and slot in with his new colleagues.

Even the normally reliable Saturn V played tricks during lift-off on 11 April 1970. A second stage engine cut off two minutes early, so the remaining four motors and the third stage had to compensate.

Nevertheless, everything seemed to be functioning beautifully during the translunar cruise. Capcom Joe Kerwin even told the crew, 'We're bored to tears down here.' Soon after, a scheduled TV broadcast ended with mission commander James Lovell looking forward to a 'pleasant evening' in the Command Module Odyssey. At the time, they were cruising 200,000 miles (320,000 km) from Earth. The calendar read 13 April.

Nine minutes later, boredom and relaxation were suddenly forgotten when there was a sharp bang and vibration. Swigert reported to Houston, 'We've had a problem.' Telemetry from the spacecraft gave a confused pattern of pressure and temperature readings, but the seriousness of the situation dawned as Lovell reported a drastic power loss with zero pressure in one oxygen tank and falling pressure in the other. From the window gas could be seen venting into space. Odyssey's fuel cells would soon fade and die, leaving the craft with only the 10-hour battery reserve needed for re-entry.

There was no question of the Moon landing going ahead. The priority now was to come up with a way to get the men home before they expired in the cold vacuum of space. The one saving grace in the crisis was that Aquarius was still attached. The Lunar Module was designed to give life support for two men over a period of 50 hours; it would now have to keep three men alive for more than 80 hours.

Their first priority was to power up Aquarius and align its guidance system before Odyssey's fuel cells gave out altogether. Six hours after the explosion, Lovell carried out the first of two LM burns introduced to speed up their return.

Urgent calculations showed that the LM carried enough oxygen to last the entire trip but there was the danger that its lithium hydroxide canisters would not cope with the build-up of carbon dioxide. In an ingenious solution, the crew attached a canister in Odyssey to the LM

environmental system using a couple of hoses, plastic bags, cardboard and tape.

Power and water supply were more of a problem. They were forced to conserve energy and cut water intake to a fifth of normal, while drinking fruit juices, and eating hot dogs and other 'wet-pack' foods.

Two hours after rounding the Moon, another engine burn boosted Unlucky 13 towards a Pacific splashdown. The remaining three days turned into an endurance test for the crew. The temperature inside Odyssey sank to 3°C, while its walls and panels were covered in condensation. Lovell later reported 'rain' falling inside the CM as it decelerated in the atmosphere!

With four hours to go, the Service Module was jettisoned, exposing Odyssey's heatshield. As they watched through the window, the amazed crew reported, 'There's one whole side of that spacecraft missing!'

Three hours later, they separated from their lifeboat, Aquarius. The way was clear for the revived CM to enter the upper atmosphere.

Mission Control Center at Houston. Apollo 13 Lunar Module Pilot Fred Haise is visible on the screen during the fourth TV transmission, which was shown on the evening of 13 April, shortly before the near-disastrous explosion. In the foreground, with his back to the camera, is Eugene Kranz, one of the four Flight Directors. (NASA)

Many prayers were offered up for the crew's safe return, but the craft was soon sighted and splashdown occurred in full view of the carrier *Iwo Jima*. President Nixon announced a national day of thanksgiving. 'Never have so few owed so much to so many,' he declared.

The Accident Review Board blamed faulty pre-launch test procedures. Warning signs had gone unheeded, so when Swigert set the oxygen tank fans in motion on 13 April, a short circuit started a fire. Within a matter of minutes, tank number two was ruptured by an explosion which also damaged the other tank and blew a hole in the side of the Service Module.

As for the crew, they were badly dehydrated, but otherwise none the worse for wear. Their total weight loss came to 31½ lb (14 kg), to which Lovell contributed an Apollo record of 14 lb (6.3 kg). None of them ever flew in space again.

THE MOUNTAINS OF THE MOON

The near-disaster to Apollo 13 resulted in a nine-month interval between missions. The Soviets took advantage by retrieving a small soil sample courtesy of Luna 16 in September 1970. Unmanned exploration of the Moon continued in November when a lunar rover, Lunakhod 1, was deposited on the Sea of Rains. Not surprisingly, the Soviets made great play of the fact that these successes had been achieved cheaply and at no risk to human life.

NASA's answer was to make its Moonwalkers more mobile, starting with a small handcart on Apollo 14. In command was former Mercury astronaut and Chief of the Astronaut Office, Alan Shepard. Now 47 years of age, he was

Alan Shepard assembles a core tube during the second Moonwalk of Apollo 14. Alongside him is the hand-drawn cart known as the Modularized Equipment Transporter. (NASA)

considerably older than any of the other Apollo astronauts. Edgar Mitchell and Stuart Roosa were both rookies, so between them, the three astronauts had clocked up just 15 minutes in space, by far the lowest total of any Apollo crew.

Thunderstorms forced a 40-minute hold in the countdown, so everything was rescheduled, enabling translunar injection to begin on time. Then came an unexpected hitch when the latches refused to bind the Lunar Module and Command Module together. Abandonment of the landing was a distinct possibility until they succeeded by using force to drive the probe home.

Three days later, Apollo 14 arrived in lunar orbit and its path was altered to bring it within 11 miles (17 km) of the surface. Separation of the LM Antares came on the twelfth revolution, but almost immediately the onboard computer went into the abort mode. The crew had to reprogram it to eliminate the fault.

Another hazard arose during the 11½-minute drop to the surface when the landing radar cut out, leaving the men 'blind' as they hovered over the rugged uplands. With an abort just seconds away, Mitchell tried flicking the switch on and off, and the radar returned to life. Antares set down in a depression which tilted it at an eight degree angle.

Delayed for 45 minutes by poor communications, Shepard finally opened the hatch and descended onto the plain. Ten minutes later, he was joined by Mitchell, and the two men busied themselves collecting samples and setting up a complex science package.

Apollo 14 carried two new experiments. The 'thumper' was a device to set off small explosions which could be picked up by an array of geophones. After a struggle, Mitchell succeeded in firing 13 of the 21 charges. Their second seismic experiment was to deploy a grenade launcher which would be activated by radio command after their departure.

The busy work schedule and clinging dust took their toll, and it was a tired twosome who clambered back into Antares nearly five hours after opening the hatch.

Their second excursion involved a one mile (1.6 km) hike to Cone crater. They found the early stages easy going, but by the second stop, it was becoming more arduous, forcing Mitchell to turn up the ventilation on his suit. The cart tended to sink into the loose surface layer, so they sometimes had to carry it. In the absence of landmarks they began to feel disoriented, resulting in several pauses to check the map and take a breather.

Each time they crested a rise their hopes were dashed, and after two hours of hard trekking they decided to give up and head back to Antares. Little did they realize that the rim of Cone crater lay less than 200 feet (60 m) away.

Back at the LM, Shepard revealed his surprise climax. Using a makeshift golf club, he struck several balls up to 1,200 feet (370 m) – 'not bad for a six iron'. The second EVA brought their total time on the surface to over nine hours. When Antares lifted off from Fra Mauro, they had collected 96 lb (43 kg) of dirt and rocks, and spent 33½ hours on the Moon.

Concern over the docking latches proved unfounded as the two craft firmly embraced at the first attempt. After unloading, the LM ascent stage was sent spiralling into the Moon. On the homeward journey, the crew were kept busy experimenting with materials processing. Splashdown in the Pacific took place within sight of the recovery ship. For the third and last time, an Apollo crew had to endure a two-week quarantine.

DRIVING AMONG THE MOUNTAINS

Although the Soviets still retained some interest in the Moon, matters were not helped by the third launch failure of the secret N-1 booster. On 27 July 1971 its engines fired for only seven seconds before the stricken giant began spinning and toppled over, once again badly damaging the pad.

The previous day, nearly a million people gathered to witness an uprated Saturn V carry aloft a heavyweight Apollo 15. The translunar cruise was uneventful apart from a water leak and the usual crop of minor alarms.

Prior to its first pass behind the Moon, the scientific instruments in the Service Module were activated ready for use by CM pilot Alfred Worden. Separation of LM Falcon from Endeavour was briefly delayed by a loose connection, but the descent was well worth waiting for as David Scott and James Irwin swooped over the 15,000-foot (4,500 m) Apennine mountains. One foot came to rest in a small crater, tilting the LM by 11 degrees. Two hours after their arrival, Scott poked his head and shoulders through the top hatch to photograph the breathtaking panorama.

Next day, the commander descended the ladder, followed shortly by Irwin. Both men were soon blackened by dust, and it became a regular chore to brush each other off so that they did not overheat.

Deploying their battery-powered rover proved more difficult than expected, then Scott found he could only use rear steering. Ready at last, they set off on a five-mile (8 km) tour along the edge of Hadley Rille. Steering through the craters and boulders, they enjoyed a 'rocking and rolling ride' as Scott put the buggy through her paces. Although top speed on the flat was only 7 mph (11 kmph), both men were glad they had seat belts.

The rover's TV camera sent back dramatic images of the sinuous rille, its sides etched in stark light and shadow and sprinkled with angular boulders. Six hours passed before they returned to the LM loaded with bags of rocks, soil and core tube samples.

A water spill in the cabin delayed the second excursion for an hour, then they were off to the Apennine foothills. Once again, the men used all their geological training as they uncovered the first green Moon rocks and large chunks of white crystalline 'Genesis rock'.

The EVA ended with Scott making a second attempt to drill holes for the heat probes, while Irwin dug a 16-inch (40 cm) deep trench. Finally they raised the Stars and Stripes, a task postponed from the previous day.

Their third outing saw a rare flash of ill-temper from Scott as he struggled to extract a nine-foot (3 m) long soil core. Samples of bedrock were hammered free during a final look at Hadley Rille, then they returned to Falcon for the closing ceremonies.

Scott used a small franking machine to cancel

the first stamps in a new US Postal Service issue on American space exploration. He then dropped a falcon's feather alongside his heavy hammer, and, just as scientific theory predicted, both hit the ground simultaneously in the lunar vacuum.

After carefully aligning the rover's camera so that it would record their departure, the crew left a small memorial which bore the names of 14 dead American and Soviet astronauts. When the hatch was finally closed their total EVA time had risen to 18½ hours. During their extended stay, they had driven 17 miles (27 km), collected 170 lb (77 kg) of samples, and taken well over 1,000 photographs.

The first televised lift-off from the Moon showed a shower of debris scattered by Falcon's sudden ascent. Once emptied, the LM was crashed onto the Moon in an impact detected by all three active seismometers. Endeavour remained in orbit for two more days, continuing the programme of scientific observations and launching a mini satellite from the Service Module.

On the return journey, Worden enjoyed a 38-minute spacewalk to retrieve two film cassettes from the instrument bay. He revelled in the sight of Irwin's head and upper torso framed against the orb of a nearly full Moon.

Despite a heavy splashdown when one of the three parachutes collapsed, the crew were quickly whisked away to the carrier *Okinawa*.

James Irwin beside the Lunar Module Falcon and the first Lunar Roving Vehicle. In the background are Mount Hadley Delta and the Apennine Mountains. Also visible in front of Falcon is the deployed Modular Equipment Stowage Assembly, where the lunar experiments were stored during flight. (NASA)

However, within a year, the sweet taste of success had turned sour. They were accused of attempting to profit from the sale of 400 unauthorized envelopes which had been franked on the Moon. The fallen heroes were reprimanded and deprived of their flight status.

DESCARTES

A series of mishaps meant that the launch of Apollo 16 was delayed until 16 April 1972. The outgoing journey was also bugged by minor irritations ranging from flaking paint to short circuits and communications break-up.

More serious was a problem with the back-up system on the CSM main engine shortly after LM Orion separated from its mother ship, Caspar. Several tense hours ensued before Mission Control decided to proceed with the landing. Orion arrived on the Descartes plateau six hours late, necessitating a postponement of the first EVA to the following day.

Further problems with the LM antenna meant that no one saw John Young clamber onto the

Descartes plain. An hour went by before he and Charles Duke set up a dish antenna to beam the first pictures back to Houston. Then one of the science experiments failed when Young tripped over a wire linking some sensors to their nuclear power source.

Their first drive in the rover began nearly four hours into the EVA. As they travelled about a mile (2 km) due west to a small crater named Flag, Young put the buggy through its paces, sending grey dust spurting from the wheels.

On the second day they explored the boulder-strewn slopes of Stone Mountain. The bone-shaking ride was so rough that the roll meter broke, causing Young to panic several times over Duke's carefree driving. Perched some 750 feet (230 m) up above the plain, they were able to stare down at the tiny Lunar Module, two and a half miles (4 km) away.

Their third trip took them to the lower slopes of Smoky Mountain and North Ray crater, where they found the largest boulders yet seen on any Apollo mission. Altogether, during a total of 20 hours on the surface, they covered more than 16 miles (27 km) and collected 213 lb (96 kg) of soil and rocks.

In an impromptu finale, Young demonstrated his ability to jump vertically upwards from a standing start. To his consternation, Duke's repeat effort ended in a slow-motion tumble onto his back. Fortunately, there was no damage to the embarrassed astronaut or to his suit.

Lunar lift-off was once again televised via the rover's camera. After docking, plans to despatch Orion into the Moon went awry when the craft began tumbling. However, another small satellite was successfully launched from the Service Module, and the main engine gave no further problems.

On the homeward leg, CM pilot Thomas Mattingly grabbed some of the limelight when he spent more than an hour outside Casper collecting film magazines while Duke watched from the open hatch. The only unusual event of the last two days was an unscheduled manoeuvre to ensure that fragments of the discarded Service Module did not land on the tiny Pacific island of Penrhyn. A pinpoint splashdown on 27 April allowed the crew to step onto the *Ticonderoga's* deck within 37 minutes of hitting the water.

Scientist-astronaut Harrison H. Schmitt examining a huge boulder during the third Moonwalk of Apollo 17. (NASA)

FAREWELL TO THE MOON

In June 1965, NASA recruited six civilian scientists, one of whom, Harrison Schmitt, was a geologist. It was decided to make use of his expertise on the final mission, so when Apollo 18 was cancelled, Schmitt was moved up to take the place of unlucky Joe Engle on number 17.

Spectators flocked to Florida to witness the only Apollo night launch. After a suspenseful two and a half hour hold in the countdown due to a computer malfunction, the watching multitudes were treated to the deafening roar and blinding fireball of a Saturn V lift-off. The trail of light was visible as far away as Cuba and the Bahamas.

Changes in the schedule soon made up for lost time, and Apollo 17 entered lunar orbit on 10 December. Challenger set down in a small, crater-pocked basin in the highlands of Taurus-Littrow, and Gene Cernan began the first EVA a little more than four hours after touchdown. The lunar landscape was soon being indented by the footprints of its eleventh and twelfth human visitors.

Once their Moon buggy was operational, they set up the flag and deployed the most complex scientific package of the entire programme. Drilling holes for the heat probes and a deep core sample proved just as difficult as on earlier missions, sending Cernan's pulse soaring to 150.

Mission Control curtailed the first drive but Cernan still managed to break a rear fender, resulting in a shower of grey dust covering the already grimy astronauts. An exhausted duo clambered back inside Challenger for their first sleep in almost 24 hours.

Next day, they assembled a makeshift fender before setting off for South Massif. Their most amazing discovery on the 12-mile (19 km) round trip came when Schmitt uncovered orange soil beside Shorty crater. The men returned to Challenger after a record 7 hours and 37 minutes outside their spacecraft.

Their final trip was to an extensive boulder field at the base of North Massif. Most notable of these was a huge split rock which dwarfed the two explorers. The rugged slopes took their toll and Cernan reported 'a couple of dented tyres' where even the wire mesh reinforcement had given way.

Mankind's first-hand investigation of the Moon culminated in the unveiling of a commemorative plaque. Beneath drawings of Earth's two hemispheres and a central Moon map were the words, 'Here man completed his first explorations of the Moon December 1972 AD. May the spirit of peace in which we came be reflected in the lives of all mankind.'

Their overall excursion time totalled more than 22 hours, nine times longer than Neil Armstrong's effort. Other records included the 240 lb (109 kg) collection of rocks, the 21 miles (34 km) they had driven, and the total duration of their stay at Taurus-Littrow – almost 75 hours.

Challenger blasted off on 14 December, leaving behind another multi-million-dollar heap of discarded equipment. An enhanced engine burn boosted the overweight LM towards a rendezvous with Ron Evans in America. The CM pilot needed two attempts to dock, but once Challenger was emptied of her precious cargo, the ascent stage was sent crashing back onto the Moon.

Two more days were spent photographing and probing its surface with radar, infra-red and ultraviolet scanners. Then it was time to bid farewell to the world which had been the focus of such intense activity for more than a decade.

On the way home, Evans took a one hour six minute stroll to collect more than two miles of film exposed in the instrument bay cameras. America skipped into Earth's upper atmosphere for a dawn splashdown on 19 December. Within an hour of hitting the water, the three explorers set foot on the deck of the *Ticonderoga*. It was the end of an era.

THE MOON ABANDONED

Apollo 17 marked the end of American interest in the Moon, but the Soviets still harboured dreams of going there one day. Early in 1972, Mishin, Glushko and others began to study ways of landing three cosmonauts on the Moon by the end of the decade. The plan called for two N-1 launches to assemble a 200 ton lunar craft in Earth orbit. The 20 ton ascent section of the lander would be able to return directly to Earth without lunar rendezvous and docking.

This ambitious project was abruptly terminated when the fourth trial of the N-1 ended in an explosion after 107 seconds of flight on 23 November 1972. Defence Minister Ustinov decided that the N-1 would never be able to fly and cancelled the programme, even though there were two more rockets waiting at Baikonur.

The final nail in the coffin came in May 1974 when Glushko replaced Mishin. On his first day in office, the new Chief Designer decided to scrap everything connected with the N-1 in favour of his own grandiose plans.

6

HOMES IN THE SKY

SALUTE TO THREE BRAVE PIONEERS

Since the days of Tsiolkovsky, people have dreamed of living in space. However, all of the space stations so far designed have been far removed from the elegant spinning wheels displayed in artists' impressions and science fiction films.

At the end of the 1960s, the Soviet emphasis switched from the abortive Moon race to orbital stations. As early as 1965, Chelomei's design bureau began work on a military space station called Almaz. It was like an advanced version of the American MOL design, with a two-man crew, a large pressurized laboratory, and a return capsule.

Delays ensued, and a group of leading designers and engineers enlisted the help of several Central Committee members to doctor a speech by Leonid Brezhnev. By inserting a passage about the positive value of orbiting space stations, they forced Chief Designer Mishin to modify his opposition to such a project.

As a result of this policy shift, work on a 'civilian' station was begun by Mishin's team, with the aim of beating the American Skylab and the Almaz into orbit. Andrian Nikolayev and Vitali Sevestyanov were taken off the lunar programme in June 1970 and reassigned to Soyuz 9. In an 18-day marathon which broke the existing Gemini 7 record, they tried out a mixture of exercises and medication in an attempt to improve adaptation to long-term weightlessness.

The new regime was not very successful: on their return, the men were so weak that they had to be carried from their capsule on stretchers and had to spend several weeks in quarantine.

Despite these problems, Mishin's bureau com-pleted their development work, and the world's first space station, Salyut 1, was sent into orbit on 19 April 1971. Four days later, a three-man crew was sent aloft in Soyuz 10 to become the new station's first occupants. Then came disappointment. A manual docking by Shatalov seemed to go according to plan, but they only remained linked for five and a half hours and the crew returned to Earth at the first opportunity, making an unprecedented night landing. Years later the Soviets admitted that the docking probe had not fully entered its housing on the station.

Controllers raised the station's orbit several times to reduce air resistance. Then on 6 June, Soyuz 11 took off for a second bite at the cherry. It should have been Alexei Leonov, Valeri Kubasov and Pyotr Kolodin who waved farewell to their friends that summer morning, but fate took a hand.

Doctors noticed a small spot on an X-ray of Kubasov's lung. Rather than simply replace the cosmonaut with another flight engineer, the State Commission decided to bring in the back-up crew. So newcomers Georgi Dobrovolsky and Viktor Patsayev joined Vladislav Volkov as the first space station occupants.

Entering a lower, faster orbit than Salyut, the cosmonauts closed the gap until they lay about six miles (10 km) from their quarry. Automatic approach took them within 330 feet (100 m), then Dobrovolsky completed the docking on 7 June, followed by the link-up of the electrical and hydraulic systems. Satisfied that everything was shipshape, Patsayev floated through the tunnel, with the others hard on his heels.

Over the next four weeks, the crew were kept busy testing the station's systems, monitoring Earth's surface and atmosphere, observing distant stars and conducting bio-medical experiments. One of their favourite experiments

The Soyuz 11 crew inside their spacecraft cabin. Note the absence of pressure suits, a fatal omission which led to their deaths during re-entry. (Novosti)

involved looking after the first 'space garden'.

Not everything went according to plan. Mishin has described 'complicated conversations with Volkov', who acted as leading spokesman for the crew. Half-way through the mission, a cable caught fire, causing the men to panic and demand an immediate return to Earth until the Chief Designer was able to calm them down.

Soon after this incident, Patsayev toasted his thirty-eighth birthday with fruit juice, and was given a much valued extra onion and lemon by his companions. Once again, 'serious troubles in the space station's systems' intervened. It was decided to bring them home a week early. On 30 June, the crew loaded their flight log, film and experimental results into the Soyuz for the trip earthward. Wearing only their woollen flight suits, they settled back in their couches, undocked from Salyut and prepared for retrofire. They had passed a record 24 days in orbit.

As their craft slowed to enter the upper atmosphere, explosive bolts fired to separate the descent module from the service module to the rear and the orbital module in front. Radio communication with the cosmonauts ceased abruptly even before the craft entered its normal blackout period. However, the parachutes and soft-landing system worked perfectly, bringing the Soyuz to Earth within sight of the waiting helicopters. Then came the shock.

When the ground rescue crews opened the hatch, they found the three men lying still and silent. They were all dead. The official cause of death was a loss of air from their cabin. Without protective pressure suits, the men had quickly lost consciousness and expired.

The simple cause of the tragedy was a ball joint in an air valve which was dislodged by the

jolt of descent-module separation. Patsayev tried to stop the leak with his finger, but to no avail. According to Mishin, the substitute crew could have used a manual drive to close the valve, but they 'forgot, or did not know, or it had been omitted from their training . . .'

Salyut 1 languished empty until it was deorbited on 11 October. A year and a half passed

Rare photograph of an early Salyut space station. The name written on its hull reads Salyut 2, but this is not the military Almaz station which later flew under that name. It seems to be the second civilian station which failed to enter orbit on 29 July 1972 when its Proton rocket went out of control. Note the folded solar panels at the front end, just behind the docking tunnel. (Space Commerce Corporation)

while the Soyuz was modified to allow future crews to wear pressure suits. From now on there was no room for a third passenger, so all subsequent ferry craft carried a two-man crew.

An attempt to launch a second Salyut failed in July 1972, but everything seemed set for another headline-grabbing expedition when the first Almaz (Salyut 2) went into orbit on 3 April 1973, six weeks before the scheduled debut of Skylab. Western observers noted that the spacecraft telemetry used military frequencies reserved for reconnaissance satellites. However, 12 days after launch, the station depressurized and had to be abandoned. Its orbit was allowed to decay until it plunged into the Indian Ocean on 28 May.

Even before the demise of Salyut 2, a replacement designated Cosmos 557 was sent into a similar 52 degree orbit. Even fewer details than normal were released, but its telemetry resembled that of Salyut 1. Unfortunately, the would-be station lost all its fuel immediately after launch and spun out of control, so it was disguised under the Cosmos label. It burnt up on 22 May, only 11 days after launch.

SHADING A CRIPPLED SKYLAB

Throughout the 1960s, there were two American competitors for space station funds. NASA wanted to use existing Apollo hardware, while the US Air Force wanted to fly a Manned Orbiting Laboratory (MOL), a modified Gemini capsule with a partly pressurized workshop. In June 1969 the Nixon Administration cancelled the military programme and seven of its 15 astronauts transferred to NASA.

However, the agency was also torn between two proposals. Von Braun's team at Huntsville favoured using an empty S-IVB rocket stage which could be equipped as a laboratory in orbit. Houston preferred a fully equipped 'dry' S-IVB which could be carried into orbit on top of a single Saturn V. This scheme had the advantages of greater simplicity and safety, and in July 1969 NASA Headquarters accepted this version, later christened Project Skylab.

On 14 May 1973, thousands of spectators gathered at the Cape to watch the final Saturn V launch. Installed on top of the booster was the 85 ton station, its solar panels folded over a thin aluminium micrometeorite shield. However, unknown to the watching multitudes, disaster struck only a minute after take-off. Air began to rush under the loose-fitting shield, tearing it from the lab along with one of the solar panels.

Only after the disabled Skylab entered orbit 270 miles (430 km) above the Earth did people on the ground realize that something had gone badly wrong. Although the solar panels on the Apollo telescope mount deployed correctly, no power was detected from the two main panels. The $2.5 billion investment in Skylab seemed to have evaporated even before the first crew set foot inside it.

Countdown for the Skylab 2 mission halted while emergency discussions took place. Meanwhile, the ailing station's internal temperature gradually increased to more than 55°C. To help cool it down, the station was turned end on to the Sun, even though this reduced the power available from the operational solar panels.

It was eventually decided to attempt a rescue mission. The first crew was given a repair kit which included a variety of sunshades and special tools. Charles Conrad, Paul Weitz and physician Joseph Kerwin set off on 25 May for a rendezvous with the unknown.

Their worst fears were confirmed as they came alongside the huge station, its skin blistered and blackened by the Sun. One solar panel was entirely missing, and the other was held back by a tangled aluminium strap. Weitz stood up in the open hatch with Kerwin grimly holding onto his legs, and spent the next hour trying unsuccessfully to pull or cut the snagged panel free with a 'pruning hook' device. Further frustration followed when the tired men had to don their pressure suits again and repair the docking mechanism. They finally struck lucky at the fifth docking attempt.

Next day, Weitz and Conrad ventured into the station. Although the atmosphere was unpolluted, the temperature in the workshop was far too high for a prolonged stay. Retreating to the airlock, they were able to push outside a boom attached to a folded parasol. Once it was far enough out, the rectangular sunshade was opened. Almost immediately, the internal temperature began to fall, and within 11 days it had reached a comfortable 24°C.

Their next job was to improve the power situation. There was no alternative but to try the pruning hook once more during a dangerous spacewalk on 7 June. While Conrad positioned the bolt cutters on the aluminium strap, Kerwin tried with all his might to cut through it. Suddenly, the strap gave way, but the panel remained firmly in place.

Only after the two men hauled on a tether tied to the panel did it break free, sending them somersaulting through space. The final seal on the remarkable four-hour EVA came when power began to surge into the dead batteries. With normality restored, the crew were able to enjoy the most luxurious onboard facilities ever provided in a space vehicle.

Skylab was three times larger than Salyut. Each man had his own sleeping compartment. There were exercise machines and a dining table equipped with hot and cold water, a zero-gravity toilet and a collapsible shower for use once a week. There was even a dartboard with Velcro-tipped darts, and magnetized playing cards which stuck to the table. The larger room provided an ideal location for weightless gymnastics.

Since there was no way to resupply Skylab, it was launched with sufficient consumables to last a three-man crew over a total of six months. Each astronaut had preselected his own six-day cycle of meals, dispensed in the correct sequence from drawers or a fridge. Special triangular shoe restraints made it easy to anchor themselves in the gridlike floor, except in the toilet area, which was solid for ease of cleaning.

Only a few minor problems interfered with their enjoyment. Sound did not carry in the low pressure atmosphere, so they were forced to use the intercom if they were more than 10 feet (3 m) apart. Orientation proved difficult and resulted in some motion sickness.

Although the initial crew griped when they felt they were being hustled into too many tasks, they soon made up for lost time, and when the mission came to an end they had obtained more than 7,000 Earth images and 30,000 pictures of solar activity. The film magazines from the solar cameras were retrieved during a one and a half

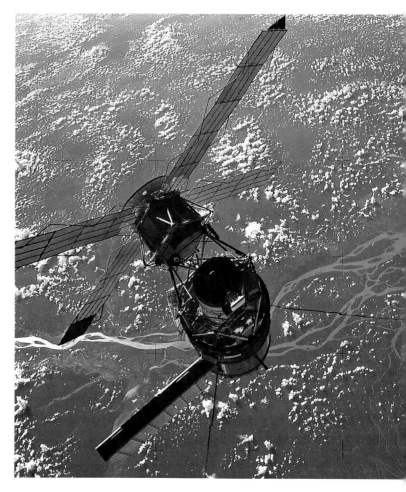

The partially disabled Skylab space station as seen by the crew of Skylab 3. The parasol heatshield deployed by the station's first occupants is just visible through the support struts of the telescope mount. Note the single remaining solar panel projecting from the side of the station. Far below is the Amazon River of Brazil. (NASA)

hour spacewalk in which Conrad repaired a faulty battery by rapping it with a hammer!

With the film, blood and urine samples safely stowed in the CSM, they returned to a Pacific splashdown on 22 June. Special 'pressure pants' were worn as a precaution against fainting on the return to normal gravity. In the event, only Kerwin, the person who had used the exercise facilities least, felt the need to inflate them. They had completed 28 days and 404 orbits around the Earth.

Due to concern over their health, the Command Module was lifted on board *Ticonderoga* with the men still inside. All three were unsteady on their feet and weight loss varied from 4 lb (1.8 kg) for Conrad to 8 lb (3.6 kg) for Weitz, with an average 3 per cent shrinkage in heart size and 14 per cent loss in red blood cells. However, all three soon made a full recovery and doctors gave the all clear for an attempt to double the endurance record.

THE SPACE ZOO

The second set of Skylab residents was launched on 28 July 1973. They too had an experienced commander in Alan Bean, a rookie pilot in Jack Lousma, and a scientist, Owen Garriott. Although none of them was a qualified physician, all three had undergone paramedic training which enabled them to examine each other every three days.

Even before the astronauts arrived at their new home, a CSM thruster assembly had to be shut down due to leaking propellant. Adaptation to their spacious environment also proved more difficult than expected. During the first

five days they all succumbed to space sickness, unable to eat and forced to resort to taking tablets and lying still.

One of their main tasks was to look after and monitor a miniature Space Age ark containing two minnows, six mice, 720 fruit fly pupae and two spiders nicknamed Arabella and Anita. Unfortunately, a short circuit in a control system caused the deaths of the mice and fly pupae. The minnows swam around in small circles, and only the spiders seemed oblivious of the change in surroundings, soon adapting to spin perfectly normal webs.

On day six a second set of CSM thrusters sprang a leak, leaving only half of the craft's four sets operable. Afraid that the problem might be

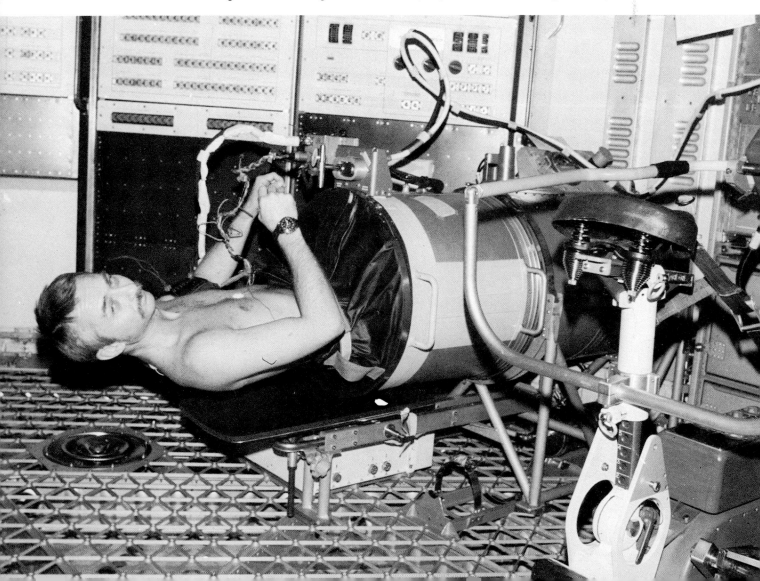

Scientist-astronaut Owen Garriott using the Lower Body Negative Pressure Device to test the effects of weightlessness. The bicycle ergometer is in the right foreground. Note also the grid-iron 'floor'. (NASA)

inherent in all of them, NASA was forced to consider a rescue mission so Vance Brand and Don Lind were put on standby.

On 6 August, Garriott and Lousma spent six and a half hours outside the station, loading film canisters in the telescope cameras, installing panels to detect micrometeorites and inspecting the CSM thrusters. They also spread a new awning over the battered parasol by pulling on lanyards so that it extended along two rods like the raising of a giant flag.

A four and a half hour EVA on 24 August saw the two astronauts plug in a replacement set of gyroscopes, reload the film in their solar telescopes and retrieve the micrometeorite panel installed 18 days earlier.

So efficient did the crew become that they thought nothing of putting in a 12 to 14 hour working day. By mid-August, they were requesting extra work to keep them busy. Their efforts were rewarded in early September when the Sun suddenly burst into violent activity. Thirty-one flares were recorded in one day, followed by a huge eruption which disrupted communications on Earth and generated a dancing aurora in the atmosphere. Fortunately, the planet's magnetic field shielded them from the deadly dose of radiation.

Forty days into the flight, doctors were heartened to discover that their physical deterioration seemed to have bottomed out. Much of the credit was given to a strict exercise regime of one hour a day. The crew were allowed a third spacewalk on 22 September. This time, Bean joined Garriott for a two and a half hour session unloading film cassettes, retrieving strips of material and cleaning a telescope.

Three days later, the crew loaded Apollo with experimental results, donned the pressure pants, and headed for the Pacific. They brought with them 16,000 photographs and 18 miles (29 km) of Earth resources data tape, the fruits of 59 days and 852 orbits around the Earth. Their partially disabled Command Module behaved well during re-entry, though it turned over after hitting the water.

Once again, the doctors pronounced themselves satisfied with their condition, especially since they adapted faster to normal gravity than

the first Skylab crew. The way was open for an even longer endurance test.

FAREWELL TO SKYLAB

The final crew comprised three newcomers. Mission commander was Gerald Carr, CM pilot was William Pogue, and Edward Gibson was the science specialist. Skylab 4 rose from Pad 39B on 16 November 1973 after a six-day postponement due to hair-line fractures in the tail fins of their Saturn 1B rocket.

Docking was completed at the second attempt, but almost immediately, Pogue had to resort to use of a sick bag, despite having taken medication. The crew discussed whether to hide the evidence, unaware that their conversation was being overheard on the ground. Chief astronaut Alan Shepard reprimanded Carr for even contemplating such a breach of regulations.

From then on, morale hit rock bottom. Ground controllers, used to the workaholic exuberance and efficiency of Bean's crew, failed to allow for the necessary acclimatization. Finding their way around the station, stowing items brought from Earth, and locating equipment proved a time-consuming and frustrating experience. The crew complained bitterly that they were being given too much to do and too many new tasks.

Gibson and Pogue earned some well-deserved praise on 22 November when they spent six and a half hours outside repairing a jammed antenna used in Earth surveys. Almost immediately one of the gyroscopes failed, making precise alignment for Earth surveys more difficult than normal. A second failure would bring the mission to an abrupt end. In order to save on fuel, the crew switched over to solar astronomy and medical experiments.

As Christmas approached, the lethargy among the crew and friction with ground controllers led to a frank discussion about how to improve matters. As a result, work schedules were adjusted and the men were given more time to relax. Welcome diversions came when the astronauts sighted Comet Kohoutek, followed soon after by a revival of the quiescent Sun.

Christmas Eve was marked by a tree fashioned from food containers and season's greetings passed on by the teleprinter. The next day was no holiday, however, as Carr and Pogue spent seven hours outside the station fixing an X-ray telescope and taking pictures of Kohoutek before it disappeared behind the Sun. The comet also provided a wonderful display for Carr and Gibson during their third EVA on 29

Waste disposal Skylab style. Astronaut William Pogue holds onto the ceiling as he prepares to jump onto a trash bag to force it into the airlock. Assisting in the operation is Gerald Carr. (NASA)

December. 'It is yellow and orange . . . just like a flame . . . one of the most beautiful sights in creation.'

Despite the continual threat posed by erratic gyroscopes, Mission Control agreed to extend the flight day by day, enabling the crew to pass the 59 days logged by Skylab 3, then the overall endurance record held by Alan Bean.

The astronauts entered the home straight a happier and more confident team. Gibson's long hours on the solar telescopes paid off on 21 January when he obtained the first pictures to show the birth of a solar flare. These images and other data were retrieved on 3 February when he and Carr spent five hours in space, bringing total EVA time for the mission to well over 22 hours.

Five days later, they packed their samples and results into the Command Module, leaving behind a 'time capsule' of food and other perishables for any future visitors. In order to extend its lifetime, the station's orbit was raised by firing the CM's thrusters.

The mission ended with a return to Earth under manual control. Skylab 4 clocked up a record 84 days in space during which the crew travelled around the planet 1,260 times and covered 34.5 million miles (55 million km), equivalent to a flight to Mars. Despite this prolonged exposure to weightlessness, the crew were in fine shape and soon adapted to normal gravity.

Hopes that the station's orbital life could be prolonged were dashed when delays in the Space Shuttle programme and increased atmospheric drag combined to send the giant ghost ship nose-diving into the atmosphere in July 1979, scattering debris across the Australian outback.

THE MILITARY AND CIVILIAN STATIONS

In the Soviet Union, the Soyuz 11 tragedy followed by the miserable failures of Salyut 2 and Cosmos 557 had left Mishin short of options. In the absence of an orbital station, the redesigned Soyuz was sent on a two-day solo test flight in September 1973. The most notice-able differences were the two-man crew and the replacement of solar 'wings' by batteries.

Soyuz 13 reverted to solar panels for its long-duration flight in December 1973. Fitted in the orbital module was an improved version of the ultraviolet telescope installed on Salyut 1. Another test of equipment intended for future space stations was an Oasis biological experi-ment. Some Earth resources photography and bio-medical tests were also carried out during the eight-day flight. The two-man crew landed in a snowstorm, but were none the worse for wear.

Another six months passed before Salyut 3 was placed into an initial 136–168 mile (219–270 km) orbit, considerably lower than Salyut 1. Western suspicions were aroused when an Air Force crew, Colonel Pavel Popovich and Lieutenant-Colonel Yuri Artyukhin, were laun-ched towards the station on 3 July 1974. On entering the station, they immediately switched to military telemetry.

Few details were released, but we now know that this was the second of Chelomei's Almaz stations. Salyut 3 was similar in size to Salyut 1, but it consisted of two cylindrical sections rather than three, and it carried only two solar panels, each attached to a spherical docking module at the rear.

Since Salyut was equipped with four cameras as well as a large solar telescope, its low flight path made it an ideal military reconnaissance platform. Confirmation came when a retrievable capsule, similar to those used by spy satellites, was released from the station after the departure of its crew on 19 July.

The next boarding party comprised another all-military crew, but Soyuz 15 was unable to dock when a control fault caused it to approach too fast from a distance of 160 feet (50 m). With only limited battery power available, Gennadi Sarafanov and Lev Demin had no choice but to abandon the attempt and return home for an emergency night landing.

After only one brief occupation, the flight of Salyut 3 was deliberately terminated on 24 January 1975. By then, the next station was already in position, having been placed in a higher orbit of 213–221 miles (343–355 km). The

similarity in orbits to Salyut 1, the reversion to mixed crews and the use of normal frequencies indicated that it was a civilian station.

This version was equipped with three solar panels, and a docking port at the front end. The rear work section was largely occupied by a solar telescope, though there was room for an exercise bicycle and a treadmill. Since there was no shower, the cosmonauts had to wash them-selves with moist, disinfected gauze cloths. One unique feature of the station was an apparatus for recycling water from the cabin atmosphere which could be reused for food preparation, drinking or washing.

Salyut 4's first occupants were launched from Baikonur on 11 January 1975. Soyuz 17 docked with the station the next day, and when Alexei Gubarev and Georgi Grechko floated into their new home, they found a welcome sign saying 'Wipe your feet.'

For the next 28 days, a Soviet record, the men were kept busy with a wide variety of astrono-mical and bio-medical experiments, including tending an automatic cultivator which contained insects and plants such as green peas. Grechko, in particular, worked overtime, and experts reckoned that he covered three miles (5 km) a day floating between instruments. Small won-der that he lost 10 lb (4.5 kg) in weight during the voyage.

The crew followed a pattern of six work days then one rest day. They ate four small meals a day, with half an hour's exercise before break-fast, an hour in mid-morning, and another hour in the afternoon. Apart from the exercise machi-nes, both men made regular use of elasticated suits which required considerable effort just to stand upright, and they wore gravity suits during re-entry.

Despite a rough landing in a raging blizzard, their craft touched down safely in a secondary landing zone. They were soon picked up and taken to the cosmodrome for a thorough medical check-up.

Nearly two months passed before Soyuz 12 veterans Lazarev and Makarov clambered into their ship on 5 April 1975, ready for a 60-day marathon. Launch seemed routine as the four strap-on boosters separated, leaving the first core stage to continue firing. As the rocket

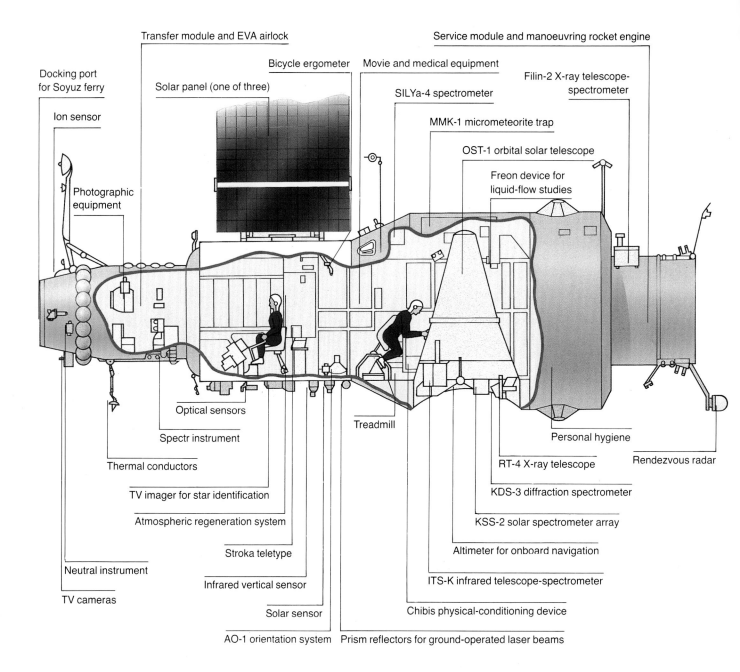

The Salyut 4 Orbital Station. (Peter Bond, based on an original published in *Sky and Telescope*)

approached an altitude of 120 miles (192 km), three explosive latches went off prematurely, severing an electrical link between the upper and lower core stages. When the second stage cut in, the lower stage was still dangling beneath, and almost immediately, the rocket began to veer off course.

The automatic abort system cut off the engines and separated the descent module, subjecting the cosmonauts to a 20g plunge towards the Earth. They came down in a mountainous region of western Siberia, about 200 miles (320 km) from the Chinese border and 1,000 miles (1,600 km) from their starting point.

On hitting the ground, their capsule rolled down a slope and skidded to a halt with its parachute tangled in some trees. The lucky duo emerged to find their capsule perched on the edge of a cliff.

Dusk was descending, so they dressed in their emergency clothing, switched on their radio beacon and built a fire. Reduced to drinking melted snow and eating a few biscuits, they were very relieved when a helicopter appeared at dawn. Their hair-raising 21-minute ride went down in history as Soyuz 18-1, or the 'April 5 anomaly'.

The Soviets blamed the near-fatal mishap on an old-style Soyuz booster, and seven weeks later they launched a second craft designated Soyuz 18. The back-up crew of Klimuk and Sevestyanov spent 60 days on board Salyut 4, second only to the final Skylab mission.

Mission controllers decided to try out a more ordered work schedule, with several consecutive days allotted to Earth photography or solar observations. Much of their time was spent using the exercise facilities and repairing faulty equipment. They were still aloft on 15 July when the Apollo–Soyuz Test Project began, so they were able to enjoy speaking with their compatriots in Soyuz 19.

Leaving Salyut 4 in automatic mode, the two cosmonauts returned to Kazakhstan loaded with 600 solar images and 2,000 pictures of the Earth. They refused to be carried from their craft, and within 15 minutes were able to walk short distances unaided. For the first few days they suffered from dizziness, nausea and general weakness, and doctors were worried by a heavy loss of red blood cells, but they recovered quickly.

Salyut 4 received one more visitor before it was deorbited. An unmanned Soyuz 20 docked with the station on 19 November 1975 for three months of joint manoeuvres before it separated for a soft landing in the Soviet Union.

HANDSHAKE IN SPACE

The final American manned flight of the decade was a joint effort with the Soviets labelled the Apollo–Soyuz Test Project (ASTP). It grew from an informal discussion between NASA Administrator Thomas Paine and Academician Blagonravov in 1970, but was quickly seized upon by both sides as a way of improving ties and cementing friendship after the Salt 1 missile treaty and the end of the Vietnam War.

A number of design changes were needed to make the two craft compatible, most notably a new American-built docking module. Another difficulty involved use of different cabin atmospheres. The Soviets agreed to reduce their air pressure and increase its oxygen content so that less time would be needed for crews to adjust while waiting inside the docking module airlock.

Starting in July 1973, a series of exchange visits was arranged, resulting in a significant breakthrough with the first American inspection of the Baikonur cosmodrome on 28 April 1975.

In order to try out their modified craft, Anatoli Filipchenko and Nikolai Rukavishnikov, the main back-up crew for the ASTP, spent six days in orbit during December 1974. Despite the new spirit of openness and co-operation, there was no prior warning of the launch. Confidence was not improved when Soyuz 16 entered the wrong orbit, though the crew were able to adjust their path and successfully try out mock docking manoeuvres before returning to the snow-covered steppe.

Not all Americans were happy with ASTP. Some thought that the mission costs were not being shared equally, and that the only side to benefit technologically from the mission was the Soviets. The Soyuz 18-1 débâcle added to fears that American lives were at risk, and Senator William Proxmire went so far as to call for a postponement. The Soviet response was predictably prickly, and NASA declared full confidence in its new partners.

First to get away was Soyuz 19, occupied by Alexei Leonov and Valeri Kubasov. A second rocket and two back-up crews were poised to take their place, but the launch went smoothly. The Soyuz orbit was eventually circularized at an altitude of 140 miles (225 km), and the crew started their biological experiments with microorganisms, fish eggs and fungi. The only disappointment was a broken antenna which blacked out TV pictures.

Seven and a half hours later, Apollo 18 blasted off from the Cape in the last launch of a Saturn rocket. In command was veteran Tom Stafford; CM pilot was Vance Brand, and Docking Module pilot was 51-year-old Donald 'Deke' Slayton, the only Mercury astronaut never to fly in space.

After entering the lowest orbit ever flown by an Apollo craft, the docking module was successfully withdrawn from inside the S-IVB, and the crew set off in pursuit of their quarry.

The historic link-up came on the third day

Painting by Robert McCall showing Apollo 18 about to dock with Soyuz 19 during the climax of the Apollo–Soyuz Test Project (ASTP). (NASA)

when Stafford edged in for a manual docking. An unpleasant smell 'like burnt glue' greeted the astronauts when they opened up the docking module, but the air soon cleared, allowing Stafford and Slayton to float inside and prepare to breach the Iron Curtain. In a sign of hope for the world, hands from East and West grasped each other in the time-honoured gesture of friendship.

Four men squeezed around a small table in the Soyuz to receive congratulatory messages from President Ford and Chairman Brezhnev. Then it was time for an exchange of flags, commemorative plaques and medals. Leonov produced tubes with vodka labels, only for his disappointed guests to discover they contained borsch.

Next day was marked by further crew exchanges during which Brand toured the Soyuz while Leonov enjoyed a meal aboard Apollo. The afternoon press conference was full of talk about détente and mutual co-operation.

With the diplomatic niceties over, it was time to carry out the experimental programme. On 19 July, Apollo backed away from the Soyuz and moved between the Soviet craft and the Sun, creating an artificial eclipse. During the redocking manoeuvre, Slayton brought Apollo in for capture slightly off centre, causing a rough linkup which led to requests for damage checks from Moscow.

Final separation came later that day, leaving both teams to carry out their individual experiments. A live TV audience saw Soyuz 19 disappear in a cloud of dust as its rockets fired to cushion the impact. After autographing their charred capsule, the returning duo were flown back to Baikonur for a press conference.

The Apollo crew continued their operations with a small onboard furnace, made astronomical observations and photographed the planet's surface until it was time for them to return.

However, re-entry on 24 July proved far from routine.

Upset by communications difficulties, Brand forgot to operate the switches which would deploy the parachutes and cut off the thrusters. When the drogue parachute did not appear on schedule he deployed it manually, but the thrusters kept on firing. Poisonous gas entered the cabin through a pressure relief valve, causing the men to gasp for breath. Brand passed out before Stafford was able to grab the oxygen masks when they hit the water.

Rescue was delayed when the CM turned over, but fortunately Brand was quickly revived. They accepted the brass band welcome on the *New Orleans*, but were immediately confined to bed for intensive medical examinations. Two weeks passed before they were released for a triumphant return to Houston.

THE END OF THE FIRST GENERATION

With no more American flights planned until the Shuttle became operational, the field was left clear for the Soviets. On 22 June 1976, Salyut 5 (Almaz 3) was sent into orbit, to be followed two weeks later by Soyuz 21 with a two-man Air Force crew. Docking expert Boris Volynov achieved a smooth link-up the next day, opening the way for a seven-week occupation of the new station.

Similar in appearance to Salyut 3, the new station was inserted into a low orbit. Although its crews were all military personnel, and its transmissions used military frequencies, it was not simply a spy platform. Volynov and Zholobov were kept busy growing monocrystals, melting new alloys, looking after fish, turtles and plants, using an infra-red telescope and conducting bio-medical tests, on top of their extensive Earth observation programme.

The cosmonauts were expected to stay aloft for several months, but Tass suddenly announced their imminent departure on 24 August. In fact, they were hurriedly brought back ten days ahead of schedule due to a 'psychological breakdown'. Not surprisingly, no official explanation was given at the time.

Sandwiched between visits to Salyut 5 was the eight-day solo flight of Soyuz 22, using a spare capsule left over from the ASTP. Its unusual orbit, inclined at 65 degrees to the Equator, enabled most of the globe to be photographed by a new East German multi-spectral MKF-6 camera system.

Next in line to occupy Salyut 5 were Vyacheslav Zudov and the first recruit from the Soviet Naval Air Force, Valeri Rozhdestvensky. Unbelievably, the jinx struck once more. A problem with their rendezvous approach system meant the mission had to be aborted – the seventh flop in eleven Soyuz docking attempts.

Soyuz 23 made an emergency night landing during a raging blizzard on 16 October 1976, but the descent module drifted off-course into the 20 mile (32 km) wide Lake Tengiz in the first splashdown of the Soviet manned programme. Alerted by the Soyuz radio beacon, ground crews rushed to the area. Frogmen were able to attach flotation collars, but rescue by boat was impossible in the partially frozen lake.

Amphibious vehicles failed to get through, so helicopters carrying searchlights were called out to haul it back onto dry land, a task hampered by high winds and snow whipping across the lake. Only after ten hours of heroic struggle was the craft beached and its exhausted, frozen crew safely extricated.

Nearly four months passed before the next crew was launched. An air problem on Salyut seemed to be confirmed when Viktor Gorbatko and Yuri Glazkov docked Soyuz 24 to the station, then waited a whole day before entering. However, when they opened the hatch the air was clear, and they settled down for a two-week stay. During this time, they repaired a computer, continued the experimental programme and used bottled gas to replace the station's atmosphere. The day after their return, a retrievable capsule was released from Salyut.

It was the end of an era of mixed fortunes. Chief Designer Mishin had already been supplanted in May 1974 by his arch-rival, Valentin Glushko. However, he did leave behind one important legacy – a new generation space station which eventually came into its own, three years after his dismissal.

7

SALUTE TO PEACE

PROGRESS

Salyut 6 was launched into space by a Proton rocket on 29 September 1977. For the first time a space station was equipped with two docking ports, one at either end. Now it would be possible to relieve the existing team before they vacated the station. A second port could also be used to receive supply ships, opening the way for missions lasting many months.

The Progress cargo craft was an unmanned version of the Soyuz spacecraft but lacking the solar panels. Forty-two of these craft were used to carry fuel and dry cargo to the Salyut 6, 7 and Mir space stations. Once emptied, they were filled with rubbish and sent to their destruction during re-entry. (Space Commerce Corporation)

Its first occupants should have been Vladimir Kovalyonok and Valeri Ryumin, but when Soyuz 25 arrived at the station's front end, the docking latches refused to hold the two craft together. After four attempts, the disappointed crew had to turn round and head for home.

Taking no chances with the forward port, Soyuz 26 with Yuri Romanenko and Georgi Grechko pulled in at the rear entrance on 11 December. Nine days later, Grechko donned a newly designed pressure suit and exited for the first Soviet spacewalk in nine years, while Romanenko remained in the transfer compartment. Poking his head out through the docking unit, Grechko reported that the system seemed in perfect working order.

Meanwhile, the impetuous Romanenko was determined to experience the wonders of spacewalking before he had to return inside. The young rookie floated out into the void, unaware that he had forgotten to attach his safety belt. Making a grab for the line, Grechko hauled his friend back in, much to Romanenko's embarrassment.

A potentially more dangerous crisis arose when they tried to repressurize the transfer section. The gauge showed that the air was escaping into space, threatening to strand them in the airlock. The only way out was to assume the instrument was faulty and proceed as normal. The gamble paid off, and they were able to enter the main workshop after an eventful one and a half hour EVA.

When Soyuz 27 arrived at the front port, Grechko and Romanenko retreated to their Soyuz ready for an emergency evacuation, but they need not have worried. Salyut 6 became the first space station to carry four men after newcomers Vladimir Dzhanibekov and Oleg Makarov proved there was nothing wrong with

the forward docking port. Fears that the 32-ton, 100-foot (30 m) long complex might be structurally unsound proved unfounded.

Another precedent was set a few days later when they swapped contour couches between craft, enabling the visitors to depart in the old Soyuz 26 while leaving behind a fresh spacecraft. The rear port was now free to receive the first Progress supply ship.

This robot craft completed an automatic docking with Salyut on 22 January 1978, two days after launch. Packed in its forward compartment was more than a ton of food, water, film and a furnace, not to mention clean clothes, mail and newspapers. The central section contained four fuel tanks as well as compressed air and nitrogen. It took more than a week to unload the dry cargo. In its place, they stashed any refuse which was cluttering up their home.

By 5 February, the station's air and fuel supplies had been replenished, and Progress 1's main engine was fired to raise the orbit. Then the craft was cast free and sent to destruction over the Pacific.

Over the next few weeks the crew installed a Splav furnace in the forward airlock for the production of new metal alloys. Much of the remaining time was spent on Earth photography, observations with an infra-red telescope, and the inevitable exercise. Relations between the crew members and the ground were sometimes strained, partly because the rest period was inevitably interrupted by minor chores and repairs.

As the Skylab endurance record loomed, the crew received their second visitors, even though there was little practical value in their mission. However, the arrival of Czech Air Force pilot Vladimir Remek signalled a new burst of propaganda.

Remek was the first of a series of Intercosmos candidates selected from different Eastern Bloc countries in July 1976. Seasoned cosmonauts suddenly found themselves bumped in favour of inexperienced foreigners who had undergone as little as 15 months of training.

The newcomer's arrival was the excuse for an

evening of celebrations, but the remainder of the week was devoted to a series of joint experiments. Gubarev and Remek said farewell on 10 March, leaving the long-term crew to mothball the station. Prior to re-entry, they wore negative pressure trousers and increased their exercise period to three hours a day.

Grechko and Romanenko returned to Earth on 16 March 1978, having spent 96 days in orbit. Every movement was an effort, even lifting a cup or turning a radio dial. Doctors reported shrunken calf muscles and reduced heart volume. However, by 20 March they were taking walks and within a few weeks they had made a full recovery.

140 DAYS

After the disappointment of being dropped from the Soyuz 26 crew, Alexander Ivanchenkov was given a new partner, Vladimir Kovalyonok, for the next long-term Salyut mission. On 17 June 1978 they floated through the station's front port to be greeted by a welcoming note.

Once again, politics took a hand. Only 11 days into the flight, they were joined by Pyotr Klimuk and Polish cosmonaut Miroslaw Hermaszewski in Soyuz 30. A similar week-long visit by East German Sigmund Jahn and Vostok veteran Valeri Bykovsky was inserted during August.

Apart from these propaganda coups, there were few noteworthy distractions for most of the 140-day marathon. During a now routine spacewalk on 29 July, the cosmonauts used the same EVA suits, adjusted for size, as their predecessors. They replaced a variety of samples and detectors attached to the station's outer skin, even working through the night with the aid of lamps.

On 2 August the Soviet Union regained the cumulative space time record from the United States, a position it has held ever since. The station was resupplied in July and August. Particularly welcome were the fresh milk, strawberries, onion and garlic to enliven their drab-tasting food, and a guitar for Ivanchenkov. The flight engineer's appetite began to play strange tricks as he became obsessed with cheese, including his partner's rations!

Their programme of smelting, Earth photography and astronomical observations continued, but attempts to grow plants met with failure apart from one onion which was eagerly sampled by the two cosmonauts. Their quality of life was further improved when Progress 4 brought work mittens, a cassette player, music tapes, electric shavers, fur boots to keep their feet warm, and room dividers to give each man some privacy.

On 2 November they headed for home in Soyuz 31 carrying their film and results. Both men were on an emotional high as they breathed fresh air for the first time in four and a half months. Kovalyonok managed to bend down and grab a handful of earth before being helped into a reclining chair. Rehabilitation was much faster than expected. Only a day after touch-down they were allowed to go swimming, and on 4 November they managed a 40-minute walk.

HALF A YEAR IN SPACE

Soyuz 32 arrived at Salyut's front door on 26 February 1979, carrying Vladimir Lyakhov, Valeri Ryumin and spare parts for the station. More equipment soon arrived in Progress 5, including a replacement Kristall furnace, centrifuges for the biological experiments, portable radios, a two-way televideo system, and a gamma ray telescope. By the end of March they had completed 38 repair jobs in addition to their scientific work.

One of their most difficult tasks was to isolate a leaking fuel tank by rotating the entire three-module complex. This generated just enough gravity to move the fuel into a reserve tank and an empty tank on the Progress. Over the next few days, the damaged tank and pipes were blown through with nitrogen, and the flight continued as if nothing untoward had happened.

They were scheduled to receive two visiting crews. Soyuz 33 blasted off on 10 April, carrying Nikolai Rukavishnikov and Bulgarian Georgi Ivanov. Everything was fine as the craft closed to within two miles (4 km), but the final engine burn cut out after just three seconds. The watching Salyut crew reported 'an unusual flame pattern' at the rear of Soyuz.

Docking was cancelled, but even more serious was the possibility of the crew being stranded in orbit. Next morning, they resorted to their back-up engine, but it refused to stop until Rukavishnikov shut it off manually after 213 seconds. When the craft dived into the atmosphere, deceleration forces of up to 10g forced the men back in their seats. Fortunately, recovery craft soon located them from the glow of their capsule against the night sky. It was Rukavishnikov's second disappointment in three flights.

Rapid re-evaluation of the long-term mission was required. There was a slim chance that Soyuz 32 was suffering from the same engine problem. The solution was to send up an unmanned ferry.

Soyuz 34 arrived under automatic control on 8 June, bringing letters and spares and a partially grown tulip. The old ferry was packed with worn-out equipment, samples and boxes of film, and soft-landed in Kazakhstan on 13 June. At least the men had a new craft with a reliable engine once more.

They settled down for the long, lonely haul ahead. Their day was split into a regular routine: roused at eight, then half an hour of exercises, shave, breakfast of canned meat, cottage cheese, bread and tea or coffee; two and a half hour morning work session followed by more exercises; dinner of soup, canned meat, mashed potatoes and juices; a brief 'leisure' period, then back to work for the next two to four hours; another hour of exercises; finally supper and leisure time during which they watched TV, spoke to their families or were entertained by a variety of celebrities.

Their greatest challenge in the entire flight involved a 33-foot (10 m) diameter radio telescope which unfurled in the rear docking tunnel as Progress 7 pulled away. Between 18 July and 9 August, the crew spent most of their work sessions operating the telescope in tandem with an observatory in the Crimea.

As the end of the mission neared, they tried to jettison the antenna, but it snagged on a docking target, blocking the rear entrance and preventing automatic attitude control. It would have to be removed. Although they were tired after five months in orbit, the men volunteered to attempt a highly dangerous repair.

On 15 August, Ryumin opened the hatch and moved along the length of the station, leaving Lyakhov to pay out his umbilical cord behind him. Dodging the viciously swinging dish, he managed to cut the wires which held it tight and then pushed with all his might until it tore free and floated away.

Ryumin celebrated his fortieth birthday on 16 August, and three days later their 175-day marathon was over. They were carried from the capsule, but within hours they were able to walk unaided. Ryumin had the distinction of weighing the same as when he had left, and both men recovered within a matter of weeks.

RYUMIN'S SECOND TIME AROUND

While an empty Salyut 6 circled the Earth, the Soviets tried out another piece of improved hardware. An unmanned Soyuz-T was launched on 16 December 1979, and spent several months docked to Salyut. Solar panels had been re-instated on the new version, giving it greater endurance. It was also lighter and more manoeuvrable, and was equipped with a digital computer and an improved landing system.

Salyut's next residents were a surprise. The original plan had envisaged Valentin Lebedev as flight engineer, but Ryumin was asked to step in when the unlucky cosmonaut damaged knee ligaments in a trampoline accident. As a result, he had the strange experience of reading a welcoming letter written by himself. However, he was able to show Popov the ropes and aid his adaptation to life in zero gravity.

Their first task was to unload Progress 8 and commence repairs. They fitted new batteries and control systems, and managed to fix the gamma ray telescope. Their first guests were not long in arriving. Hungarian Bertalan Farkas was welcomed by the traditional 'loaf', made from 50 bite-size breads, and three salt pills.

Hardly had one set of visitors departed than they were paid a fleeting visit by Yuri Malyshev and Vladimir Aksyonov during a test flight of Soyuz T-2. After three days of joint flight, the trial ended with separation of the orbital module prior to retrofire, thereby saving fuel.

The non-stop activity continued with the arrival of Progress 10 on 1 July, quickly followed by Viktor Gorbatko and Vietnamese Air Force officer Pham Tuan. Much play was made of the fact that the 'guest' cosmonaut had shot down a B-52 in the Vietnam conflict and was now photographing war damage to his country.

Hard on the heels of the first spaceflight by a citizen of a Third World country came another visitor likely to irritate the United States government. Apart from being a Cuban Air Force officer, Arnaldo Tamayo-Mendez also had the distinction of being the first black spaceman.

Omission of the Soyuz exchange gave advance notice that the six-month odyssey of Popov and Ryumin would soon be drawing to a close. Progress 11 arrived on 30 September, but although the crew unloaded its stores, they knew that they would be used by another team. An intensive exercise programme preceded their re-entry on 11 October 1980 after 185 days in orbit.

Valeri Ryumin had clocked up nearly a year in space without suffering any lasting ill-effects. Within a day of landing, the crew were able to take their first walk, and they were soon fit enough to play tennis. Both men had achieved another space first by actually putting on weight.

The other flight statistics were just as impressive. The cosmonauts had taken almost 4,500 photographs and 40,000 spectrograms of the planet's surface and atmosphere. In addition, nearly 100 samples of new materials, chiefly semiconductors, had been made in the onboard furnaces.

Although Salyut 6 was almost on its last legs, two more missions were scheduled for the station. The first three-man Soviet crew for nine years linked up with the complex on 28 November. Leonid Kizim, Gennadi Strekalov and Oleg Makarov (on his fourth flight) spent most of their two-week session doing repair jobs, though they were able to try out a new holographic camera and make a few smeltings.

Salyut's fifth and final resident crew went up in Soyuz T-4 on 12 March 1981. Alongside Vladimir Kovalyonok was newcomer Viktor Savinykh, who had the distinction of being the hundredth space voyager.

The Salyut 6 space station was the first of its kind to be equipped with two docking ports, one at either end. (CNES/ Intercosmos)

Priority in the first weeks was given to repairs and maintenance. One of their main tasks was to repair the control system on one of the solar panels. Once achieved, the internal temperature rose back to normal from its previous low of 10°C.

Once Progress 12 was unloaded, the way was clear for another Intercosmos mission. Vladimir Dzhanibekov was given the job of looking after Mongolian Army captain Jugderdemidiyn

Gurragcha. Two months later, it was the turn of Romanian Dumitru Prunariu in the last of the old Soyuz series.

On 26 May, Kovalyonok and Savinykh mothballed the station, loaded their ship and returned to Kazakhstan after almost 75 days in orbit. But Salyut 6 was not finished yet. On 19 June it was joined by Cosmos 1267, a prototype of a future multi-purpose space tug and add-on laboratory. During the next six weeks, the 20 ton craft's engines were fired several times to alter Salyut's orbit.

The two craft eventually plunged into the atmosphere on 29 July 1982. The remarkably durable Salyut had been occupied for almost half of its 676 days in flight, playing host to five long-term and 11 short-term crews.

THE ARRIVAL OF SALYUT 7

Salyut 7 was virtually identical to its predecessor with minor improvements such as electric stoves, a constant supply of hot water, and a refrigerator.

Its first occupants, Anatoli Berezovoi and Valentin Lebedev, arrived on 14 May 1982. Within a week they had performed a space first by hand-launching a small amateur radio satellite called Iskra 2 from the lab's airlock. Five weeks later they received their first visitors. Occupying the third seat on Soyuz T-6 was Frenchman Jean-Loup Chrétien, the first West European cosmonaut.

Pilot Dzhanibekov had to dock manually after a computer problem, but the rest of the week went well, particularly when Chrétien produced his specially prepared French cuisine. Events in Afghanistan and Poland made this a politically sensitive visit, so while the Soviets gave banner headlines to the mission, the French were content to emphasize their scientific programme.

Alone once more, the cosmonauts took a two and a half hour spacewalk on 30 July to test future space assembly operations. Another propaganda coup followed in August when Svetlana Savitskaya became only the second woman in space, almost a year ahead of Sally Ride's trip aboard the US Shuttle. She had to

endure some mild teasing from her four male colleagues, but usually gave as good as she received. Berezovoi and Lebedev delighted her with the results of their artificial fragrance experiments – the station was filled with the smell of roses.

For the remainder of the 211-day marathon, the crew were left alone to tend their Oasis garden, photograph the Earth, use the X-ray telescope and smelt materials in the Korund furnace. Most enjoyable of all was their success in growing radishes, cucumbers, wheat and peas. A major breakthrough came when an arabidopsis plant grew to maturity and produced seeds.

By October, the crew were dreaming of home, but they gamely volunteered to continue for a few weeks more. Progress 16 replenished their stores, and a few days later, they launched a second Iskra satellite. Their heroic seven-month endurance test ended in dense fog and blinding snow on 10 December. One recovery helicopter crash-landed, but the crew were able to set off flares to guide in a second chopper. Planes carrying survival gear were waved off due to the treacherous conditions, so the returning heroes were forced to spend their first night back on Earth huddled in a tractor cabin.

Once again, their list of achievements was impressive, but Lebedev's diary illustrated the insomnia, homesickness and other psychological problems which arise during such long periods of isolation. Indeed, he and Berezovoi had soon fallen out and spent the first four months hardly speaking to each other!

COSMOS 1443

In March 1983 the arrival of Cosmos 1443 almost doubled the size of the complex. Stashed inside the newcomer were three tons of cargo, including extra solar panels for Salyut. At its front end was a descent capsule capable of returning 1,100 lb (500 kg) safely to Earth.

As expected, a new resident crew was launched on 20 April in Soyuz T-8. However, Vladimir Titov, Gennadi Strekalov and Alexander Serebrov were not destined to dock with the station. The Soyuz rendezvous radar antenna

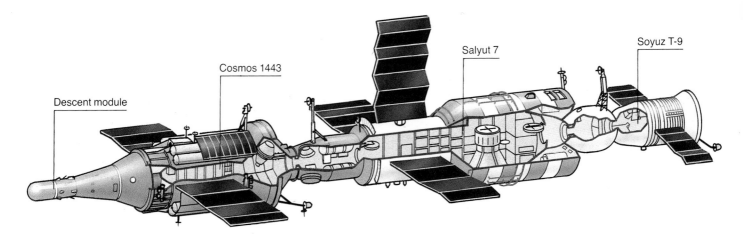

The Cosmos 1443–Salyut 7–Soyuz T9 orbital complex.
(Based on original by Teledyne Brown Engineering)

failed to deploy and attempts to free it by wiggling the craft made no impact.

Titov asked for permission to try the first 'seat-of-the-pants' docking with a space station. Using only visual aids and voice instructions from the ground, the commander edged towards Salyut, but as night approached, the Soyuz drifted out of range of the ground stations. Titov switched on the searchlight, but, with the huge bulk of the station looming in his sights, he suddenly realized that they were about to collide. In desperation, he fired the thrusters to send his craft skimming past the station. There was no choice but to carry out an emergency touchdown.

After a two-month delay, the Soviets sent up Soyuz T-9, bringing the total weight of the complex to around 47 tons. Vladimir Lyakhov and rookie Alexander Alexandrov began their occupation by unloading the Cosmos descent module. With both ports occupied, there was no opportunity to send up another supply craft, so during August they began to pack exposed film and worn-out equipment into the Cosmos. Undocking of the module was completed on 14 August, signalling a return to more normal activities.

Progress 17 arrived a few days later, but during refuelling, one of the propellant lines sprang a leak. Even worse was to follow as the unlucky Titov and Strekalov once more failed to link up with the orbiting lab. A fire broke out at

the base of their booster only 90 seconds before take-off. With the rocket about to explode, the launch director ordered an abort, catapulting their capsule into the air. The men had to endure forces up to 17g, but the escape system saved their lives and brought them safely back to earth two miles (3 km) from the blazing pad.

There was no alternative but to extend the ongoing mission. Although they had not been trained for the job, Lyakhov and Alexandrov were asked to install the extra solar panels. During two spacewalks on 1 and 3 November, the men anchored themselves in position and carefully extended the panels, one on either side of the main upright 'wing'. They eventually returned to Earth on 23 November, some five weeks later than intended.

During their 150-day sojourn, Salyut's fuel system sprang a leak, so a difficult repair job was added to the flight plan of their successors, Leonid Kizim, Vladimir Solovyov and physician Oleg Atkov. Their first visitors arrived in Soyuz T-11 on 4 April 1984. This latest international flight was enlivened by the exotic food, oriental music and yoga practised by Indian Rakesh Sharma. Space history was made a few days later when a Shuttle launch brought the number of people in orbit to 11.

An intensive series of EVAs began after equipment for fixing the propulsion system arrived in Progress 20. A work platform was automatically deployed at the station's rear ready for the repair work, enabling the crew to fit a folding ladder and install their tool boxes.

Over the next ten days, the crew exited three more times to fit two new conduits to the back-up fuel system. Two side panels were added to another of the main solar arrays during a fifth excursion on 18 May, a task completed in half the time taken by the inexperienced Lyakhov and Alexandrov.

This remarkable sequence ended on 8 August when Kizim and Solovyov spent five hours sealing off the leaking fuel pipe. The hard-pushed crew had finally restored the station to normal working order after almost 24 hours outside the station, three times the figure for the entire Soviet manned programme prior to November 1983.

Sandwiched between these repair sessions was a fleeting visit by experienced space chauffeur Dzhanibekov, test pilot Igor Volk, who was training to fly the new Soviet Shuttle, and Svetlana Savitskaya.

The redoubtable lady achieved another record when she and Dzhanibekov spent nearly four hours outside Salyut trying out a hand-tool for welding, soldering and cutting metal plates. Not only was she the first woman to go twice into orbit, but she also became the first of her sex to walk in space.

By September, the resident duo began to wind down their activities, carefully monitored by Dr Atkov. On 2 October, after almost 237 days in zero gravity, the men were gingerly lifted from the descent capsule into special chairs. Several weeks passed before they were fit enough to face a press conference and an award ceremony led by President Chernenko.

REVIVING A DEAD SPACE STATION

Salyut 7 continued to prove more unreliable than its predecessor. All telemetry from the empty station soon ceased – evidence that it had become a cold, lifeless shell.

Mission controllers decided to gamble on a daring rescue. Soyuz T-13 was launched on 6 June 1985 with a repair crew of Vladimir Dzhanibekov, now on his fifth space voyage, and Viktor Savinykh. Using all his experience of manual docking, Dzhanibekov edged his craft towards the rotating target as his partner called out distance and speed. The vital link-up was achieved two days after blast-off.

Uncertain of what awaited them, the cosmonauts donned gas masks before floating into the laboratory. Their torches showed no sign of life: the cabin temperature was below zero, there was no power in the batteries and even the drinking water was frozen.

Although the situation seemed hopeless, the men fixed up a temporary ventilation system and tried connecting each battery in turn to the solar panels. Power began to surge back into the dead batteries as the station turned towards the Sun, enabling telemetry to be transmitted and assessed on the ground. The cause of the breakdown was traced to a faulty sensor which cut off the batteries' power supply as soon as recharging began.

In the first few days, despite their fur boots, hats and mittens, the cosmonauts were forced to retire to the Soyuz every 40 minutes for warmth. They improvised a stove from a metal container and a powerful photographic lamp, but water was strictly rationed until the tanks began to defrost. By 13 June, the thrusters were back in action, opening the way for a delivery of supplies by Progress 24. The station had been saved.

A craft labelled Cosmos 1669 docked at the rear port on 21 July, but it was simply a Progress vehicle which had been given a name change in case it failed to link up. More significant was the spacewalk carried out on 2 August to install extra solar panels, bringing Salyut's third main 'wing' up to the same specification as its two fellows.

Work continued along normal lines until the arrival of Soyuz T-14 on 18 September. In a radical change of policy, the Soviets announced that there would be a partial exchange of crews. Savinykh was to stay on board and be reunited with his former team mates Vladimir Vasyutin and Alexander Volkov. Dzhanibekov was allowed to return to Earth alongside Georgi Grechko, the Soyuz T-14 flight engineer.

Within a few days, the orbital complex had been greatly enlarged by the addition of the 20 ton Cosmos 1686. Few details were released about the mystery craft, though it was revealed that its descent module contained an array of telescopes.

Everyone expected the fresh resident crew to spend many months aloft, but on 13 November, eavesdroppers in the West picked up unusual scrambled communications. A week later, it was all over. In the first case of its kind, the flight was terminated early due to Vasyutin suffering from kidney inflammation and fever. Savinykh became acting commander during the final days of the mission.

Salyut 7–Soyuz T-14 as seen from the departing Soyuz T-13. By this time, the space station had extra pairs of solar panels attached to each of its three main 'wings'. (CNES/Intercosmos)

MIR: COSMIC BUILDING BLOCK

Although Salyut 7–Cosmos 1686 were still circling the Earth, the Soviets were in a hurry to send up a more modern version. On 20 February 1986, a 'third generation' station known as Mir (Peace) was launched by Proton from Baikonur.

Mir was the first building block in what would eventually become a huge modular complex. Living conditions on the new station were much less cramped because most of the scientific equipment would be brought up later inside the add-on sections.

Mir's first occupants were the world endurance record holders, Kizim and Solovyov. However, their stay was short-lived. On 5 May, they re-entered Soyuz T-15, pulled away from Mir and dropped into a lower, faster orbit which enabled them to close the 1,900 mile (3,100 km) gulf between them and Salyut 7. Next day they completed the first transfer between space stations, and settled into their second home.

More history was made on 28 and 31 May when they sent back the first live TV pictures of Soviet spacewalks. Viewers saw them unfold and extend a frame up to a height of 50 feet (15 m) in a test of new space construction techniques. The second session ended with a welding test using the multi-purpose tool. Their eighth spacewalk brought the duo's overall EVA time to 31 hours 40 minutes.

The transfer back to Mir was completed on 26 June, and three weeks later their mission came to an end after a 'mere' 125 days in orbit. Nevertheless, their combined space time had risen to a new record of 737 days. Salyut 7–Cosmos 1686 remained aloft until they succumbed to atmospheric drag, scattering their remains across the Argentina–Chile border on 7 February 1991.

During Mir's temporary evacuation, the Soviets tested a modified ferry with a new approach and docking system, better parachutes and a more reliable engine. The first manned use of the revamped vehicle came on 6 February 1987 when Yuri Romanenko and Alexander Laveikin blasted off in Soyuz TM-2. They were kept occupied unloading two Progress vehicles and carrying out Earth remote sensing, but their real scientific programme could not begin until the arrival of Mir's first add-on module.

The Kvant (Quantum) astrophysics observatory was launched on 31 March. It consisted of a transfer tunnel and a pressurized laboratory together with a scientific payload of one ultra-violet and four X-ray telescopes. It also carried a set of gyroscopes, vital for orientating the Mir complex, and an oxygen generation unit.

Five days later, the crew watched anxiously from their Soyuz as the giant newcomer glided to within 660 feet (200 m) of Mir's aft port, then its approach system 'lost' the station, causing it to drift aimlessly away. A second attempt on 9 April ended with the two vehicles linked, but not tightly docked. Mission Control decided to send the cosmonauts outside to investigate. By backing Kvant away as far as possible without actually separating, the crew were able to remove the cause of the obstruction, a small white bag which had somehow intruded into the docking mechanism during work on the ground.

Although Mir's tanks were replenished by pumping fuel from Progress 29 through pipes on Kvant, the power supply was now inadequate for two modules. During two spacewalks on 12 and 16 June, the men spent more than five hours installing and unfolding a third solar array brought up inside Kvant.

The next round of visiting 'guest' cosmonauts began with the arrival of Syrian Muhammed Faris on 24 July. It was the first docking of a Soyuz at the Kvant port. Then came the sudden announcement that Laveikin was suffering from an irregular pulse and so he would be replaced by Alexander Alexandrov. When the disappointed cosmonaut returned on 30 July, he had been in orbit for 174 days.

The Mir base block has six docking ports, five in a cylindrical module at the forward end and one more at the rear. Although similar in size to the previous Salyuts, it is more spacious inside due to the relative absence of scientific and experimental equipment. (CNES/ Intercosmos)

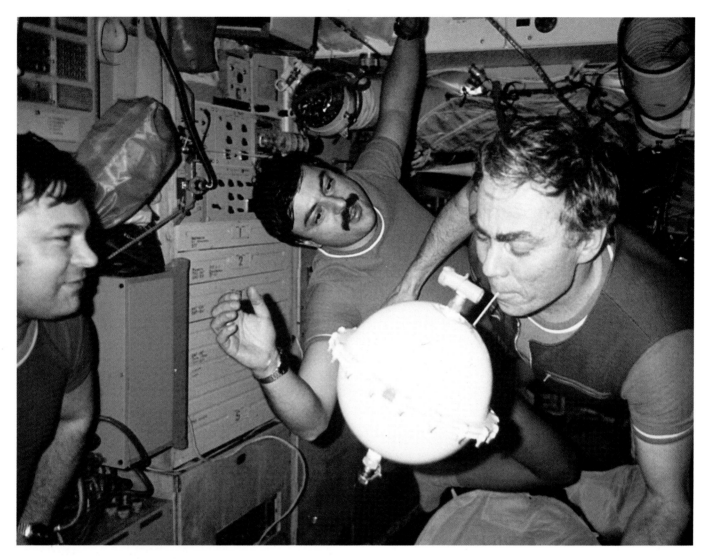

The new pair of Romanenko and Alexandrov recommenced their programme of remote sensing, plant experiments and supernova observations. As Romanenko passed the old space endurance record, his work rate declined and he began to complain of fatigue, sleeplessness and irritability. The weary cosmonaut suffered a rough landing on the frozen, windswept steppe, and had to be stretchered to a waiting helicopter, but he was none the worse for his 326 days aloft.

The last space marathon was entrusted to Vladimir Titov – at last safely on board – and Musa Manarov. By mid-January they were fully adapted to zero gravity and well into their observations with the Kvant telescopes. Progress 34 called in on 22 January 1988, bringing a new solar panel for the array erected by Romanenko and Laveikin the previous summer.

This was successfully installed during a four and a half hour EVA on 26 February.

The experimental routine continued uninterrupted apart from a procession of Progress craft and the June visit of Bulgarian Alexander Alexandrov. Unfortunately, one of the X-ray detectors on Kvant had been only partially operational for some time, so it was decided to attempt a repair even though it was not designed for such in-orbit maintenance.

Carrying a new detector and special tools

brought up in Progress 36, the men floated to the rear of Kvant and cut open the thermal blanket. Hindered by a lack of footholds, they fell well behind schedule and their efforts were finally abandoned when a vital wrench broke.

Soyuz TM-6 brought an unusual crew to the station on 31 August. Alongside Vladimir Lyakhov were Afghan Abdul Mohmand, with only six months of training under his belt, and physician Valeri Polyakov.

After the usual week on board, Lyakhov and Mohmand strapped themselves into Soyuz TM-5, undocked, and released the craft's orbital module prior to retrofire. However, when they initiated the braking manoeuvre, nothing happened. Still pondering the reason for their predicament, the crew were even more startled when the engine suddenly began to fire, forcing Lyakhov to intervene manually.

Three hours later they tried again, but the engine only operated for six seconds. Lyakhov broke all the rules by trying to complete the job under manual control, but it cut out again after only one minute. Stranded in orbit for a whole day without a proper waste management system, and saving their rations in case they landed off course, the crew breathed a great sigh of relief when their fifth retro attempt brought them safely home.

Despite their long, tiring stay aloft, the Mir crew were allowed a second repair attempt on Kvant's disabled X-ray detector on 20 October. This time, using a new set of tools and improved spacesuits, they quickly succeeded in installing its replacement.

November saw the return of Jean-Loup Chrétien, accompanied by Alexander Volkov and Sergei Krikalev. The highlight of his four-week mission, the longest ever made by a 'guest' cosmonaut, was the first spacewalk by a non-Soviet or non-American. Plans to deploy a folded antenna went awry when it refused to budge, so Volkov gave it a friendly kick and the structure opened up!

Titov and Manarov handed over the station before returning with Chrétien after 366 days in orbit, but their triumphant homecoming was delayed when the Soyuz computer overloaded and cancelled retrofire. Ground control blamed new software and used a back-up program to send them Earthward three hours late and some distance from the planned landing site.

THE EXPANSION OF MIR

The return of Titov and Manarov marked a major change in Soviet policy. Instead of aiming to extend human endurance still further, the new crew's main task was to oversee the expansion of Mir while Polyakov monitored their health.

However, the programme was dogged by postponements and delays in completing the two additional modules. Finally, the Soviets announced that Mir would be left empty when the current crew returned on 27 April 1989. Polyakov had spent nearly eight months in orbit, three months longer than his companions.

The station continued under automatic control as the first Progress M arrived on 25 August. This updated version could carry more cargo, had two solar 'wings', and employed a modern rendezvous and docking system. It was also the first of its class to dock at Mir's forward port and carry out refuelling.

The station was eventually reactivated by Alexander Viktorenko and Alexander Serebrov on 8 September. After yet another delay, Mir's second add-on section left the ground on 26 November, but one of its solar panels failed to open fully, threatening the docking. Matters were only rectified by rolling the 20 ton spacecraft while rotating its errant panel.

Then Kvant 2's onboard computer decided its approach speed was too high and cancelled the link-up. Fortunately, the second attempt on 6 December proved successful. Two days later, in a unique transfer operation, a remote arm on the module was clamped in place on Mir's front end and used to swing the 40-foot (12 m) long craft round to a side port.

Kvant 2 was to improve onboard living standards, with its shower, water and oxygen regeneration equipment, and large EVA hatch. When Progress M-2 arrived, carrying an American crystal growth experiment, the overall mass of the five-piece complex rose to about 70 tons.

Mir with Kvant 1 and Soyuz TM-9 at the rear (right) *and Kvant 2 pointing downwards. The loose thermal blankets on the Soyuz can be clearly seen. Inset is a view of the first trials of the Soviet Icarus Manned Manoeuvring Unit.* (Space Commerce Corporation)

1990 began with two spacewalks postponed from the previous April. The crew exited from one of the vacant docking ports on Mir and floated to Kvant 1, where they installed two large star sensors. Then on 11 January they tidied up Mir's hull and prepared for the arrival of the next module.

Two weeks later, they exited from Kvant 2's large hatch to test their improved EVA suits. On 1 February, Serebrov performed the first trials of a Soviet manoeuvring unit, during which he propelled himself up to 100 feet (33 m) from the station, even though he was hampered slightly by the need for a safety line. Viktorenko was given his chance to perform the same exploits four days later.

A replacement crew arrived for the next six-month stint on 13 February, leaving the way clear for an exchange of spacecraft. Bad weather delayed the return by 24 hours, enabling Serebrov and Viktorenko to clock up 166 days in orbit.

No sooner had they gone than their successors, Anatoli Solovyov and Alexander Balandin, discovered that three large thermal blankets on Soyuz TM-9 had come loose. Not only did this cause a rise in the spacecraft's temperature but it threatened to affect the sensors which controlled re-entry.

More delays hit the programme when launch of the third module, Kristall, was postponed until 31 May. Even then its final approach had to be cancelled when one of its thrusters malfunctioned. Docking was eventually achieved on 10 June, and the next day Kristall was moved to a position directly opposite Kvant 2.

Among its unique features were two extendable solar panels capable of being completely removed, and two docking ports which were designed for use by the Soviet Shuttle. Inside the mini-factory was a wide range of apparatus including five different furnaces.

On 17 July, the cosmonauts exited from Kvant 2 to carry out their Soyuz repairs. Such was their haste that they released the safety latch before the air was completely vented into space, causing the hatch to slam back against its hinges.

Moving into position and installing the ladder took more time than expected, but they succeeded in securing two of the loose blankets and headed back to the hatch. Elation turned to dismay when they discovered that the damaged door would not close. The EVA had extended to seven hours before they sealed and repressurized Kvant 2's middle compartment.

Later examination of the hatch showed its hinges were bent, but the cosmonauts managed to close it by brute force. Their time on Mir came to an end on 9 August after 179 days. Repair of the hatch was entrusted to the Soyuz TM-10 crew of Gennadi Strekalov and Gennadi Manakov, but the newcomers found the job was beyond their capability.

One significant advance came at the end of November when Progress M-5 returned film and samples to Earth by releasing a recoverable capsule prior to re-entry. Soon after, the crew prepared to greet their first paying guest, Japanese TV journalist Toyohiro Akiyama, accompanied by a replacement crew of Viktor Afanasyev and Musa Manarov. Chain-smoker Akiyama did not much enjoy his week of weightlessness.

The newcomers spent five hours outside, fixing Kvant 2's door. Two more EVAs during January 1991 installed some telescopic cranes which would later be used to move the solar panels from Kristall to Kvant 1, thereby clearing the way for a docking by the Shuttle Buran.

As Mir entered its sixth year in orbit, the Soviet press began to comment on the amount of time spent replacing worn-out equipment and questioning whether it gave value for money. Further problems arose when Progress M-7 failed to dock, then almost crashed into the station's outstretched panels.

The near-disaster was blamed on a rendezvous antenna which had been kicked during a spacewalk, so the crew had to transfer their Soyuz to the rear to enable the Progress to pull in at the front end. Further disappointment followed when the supply craft failed to return its recoverable capsule.

After a visual check of the damaged antenna on 25 April, the crew prepared to greet Briton Helen Sharman, only the third woman ever to fly on a Soviet spacecraft. A failure of the automatic approach system meant that Soyuz TM-12 had to dock manually, then a computer failure caused Mir's solar panels to drift regularly into shadow, leaving it to rely on battery power. The week-long visit was also marred by Soviet grumbles about the lack of British financial backing. A further setback came on 17 June when a small MAK satellite failed to operate after being launched through Mir's airlock.

The incoming crew of Anatoli Artsebarski and Sergei Krikalev had to carry out five spacewalks in little more than a month, spending almost 30 hours outside the station. Starting on 24 June, they succeeded in replacing the broken rendezvous antenna and began using the telescopic arm to move around the station and install an experimental girder. By their fourth EVA on 19 July, the men were ready to assemble the 46-foot (14 m) long structure on Mir's outer surface – an operation which was eventually completed eight days later. The last of the EVAs was marred by the fogging of Artsebarski's visor, so that Krikalev had to complete the work hastily and guide his companion back to the safety of the airlock.

The configuration of Mir from 1990 to 1995, showing Kristall and Kvant 2 on opposite sides of the forward docking section.

In mid-August, an attempt to release an inflatable probe from Progress M-9 failed when it sprang a leak. The remainder of the mission was taken up with the usual smeltings, photography and astrophysical observations, and testing of a Coca-Cola can.

Economic pressures led to the cancellation of a mission scheduled for November, so Soyuz TM-13 arrived carrying Alexander Volkov and two rookies, Kazakh researcher Takhtar Aubakirov and Austrian Franz Viehboeck. The five-month mission of Artsebarski ended on 10 October with the two guests seated alongside. As the only available flight engineer, Krikalev was obliged to continue aloft with Volkov for a further six months. Down below, the entire programme lay under a black cloud of uncertainty as the Soviet Union began to fragment into separate republics. Spiralling costs meant that the crew had to spend up to nine hours a day out of touch with Earth. The 'stranded' cosmonaut eventually returned home to a country with a new name and a new government on 25 March 1992 after 312 days in orbit.

8

GLIDING TOWARDS THE FUTURE

A REUSABLE SPACECRAFT

The idea of building a spacecraft which could be flown time and time again was not new. Back in the 1950s, Wernher von Braun had come up with a rocket on top of which was perched a delta-winged, piloted vehicle. By the early 1960s, the US Air Force and NASA were flying X-15 rocket planes to the edge of space, and the military were keen to develop winged space-planes. The first group of potential USAF astronauts was selected in March 1962, among them a young test pilot by the name of Neil Armstrong, but the Dyna-Soar project was cancelled the following year.

Nevertheless, interest in the potential of more economical space ferries continued. In 1967 the President's Science Advisory Committee recommended further studies on such launch systems, and several aerospace companies began to look at possible design concepts. This process accelerated in 1969 when NASA issued contracts for feasibility studies of reusable launchers.

Early designs favoured two-stage systems with orbiters carried towards space on the back of a larger delta-winged booster. Once the orbiter had been released, the crew of the booster would return to base ready for the next mission. However, such novel schemes were far too costly, so the agency turned to smaller, less expensive alternatives.

NASA's cut-price solution was to shrink the orbiter by storing its fuel in an external tank which could be thrown away once it was empty. The extra kick necessary to get into orbit would be provided by two solid fuel boosters which would fall away after use and parachute into the ocean, where they would be salvaged for future flights.

On 6 January 1972, President Nixon gave the go-ahead for development of the Space Shuttle. Six months later Rockwell International was chosen to build the orbiter and integrate it with the other elements of the launch system. Over the next nine years, several thousand contractors and some 50,000 people set about creating the world's first reusable spaceship.

NASA hoped that each orbiter would be able to fly up to 100 missions in its operational lifetime, with a turn-around time between flights of only a few weeks. In order to protect the Shuttle from atmospheric heating during multiple re-entries, new thermal insulation materials had to be developed and glued onto the craft's exterior. Most difficult of all to create was a Shuttle main engine which would be reliable, efficient and reusable.

The Shuttle prototype, Enterprise, was unveiled to the public on 17 September 1976. The following February, the stripped-down test vehicle was lifted onto the back of a 747 Jumbo aircraft for its first flight tests. On 18 June 1977, Fred Haise and Gordon Fullerton initiated its manned test phase which culminated in a series of drop tests starting on 12 August. By the end of 1978, every phase of a Shuttle launch had been simulated, and hopes were high that the first orbital flight could take place the following year.

In fact, delay followed delay. Although the first operational Shuttle, Columbia, arrived at Cape Canaveral in early 1979, the launch date

Astronauts John Young (left) and Robert Crippen occupy their seats on the upper deck of the Shuttle Columbia. Only two crew flew on the first four test flights of the Shuttle orbiter, and they were provided with ejector seats as well as orange-coloured pressure suits. (NASA)

continued to fall back until NASA finally settled for March 1981. Further niggling problems pushed the date back to 10 April, but the countdown ground to a halt at T−9 minutes when one of the five onboard computers malfunctioned. So it was that the maiden Shuttle flight was rescheduled for 12 April, the twentieth anniversary of Gagarin's momentous journey.

TESTING COLUMBIA

NASA had decided that there would be four test flights flown by two-man crews before the Shuttle could be declared operational. The men entrusted with the dangerous initial trial were veteran John Young and former MOL astronaut

Robert Crippen. Over one million spectators flooded into Florida to witness the birth of a new era in space transportation. This time they were not disappointed.

Seconds before lift-off, the orbiter's main engines roared into life, followed by brilliant flame and billowing clouds of steam and smoke as the two solid rocket boosters (SRBs) ignited. Crippen's heartbeat raced to 130 as the vehicle cleared the tower and headed out over the ocean. A little more than two minutes into the flight, the SRBs died and fell away, leaving Columbia, still attached to the huge white fuel tank, to continue into orbit. Main engine shut-off was achieved about eight minutes after lift-off, followed by separation of the fuel tank. It remained only for the small manoeuvring engines to place Columbia in a near-circular orbit about 165 miles (270 km) above the Earth.

The astronauts' delight was tempered when they opened the payload bay doors, exposing the radiators which released excess heat into space. They noticed that 16 thermal tiles had been dislodged and many more damaged by the shock waves which blasted the Shuttle on ignition. Top-secret cameras were trained on the Shuttle's vulnerable belly before NASA officials declared that the crew were in no danger.

The crew checked out the onboard systems during two days in orbit, then donned their pressure suits for the glide back to Earth. Columbia's arrival over Edwards Air Force Base in California was marked by a double sonic boom, followed by a pinpoint touchdown on the desert runway. Young and Crippen thus became the first American astronauts to return on dry land.

Although the remaining three test flights followed similar flight profiles, there were subtle differences. STS-4 stayed in orbit a week, and bad weather at Edwards forced the third mission to spend an eighth day aloft before returning to a back-up runway at White Sands, New Mexico.

Turn-around times between missions were steadily cut, so that, by the fourth mission in June 1982, Columbia only spent 42 days in the Orbiter Processing Facility at the Cape. Loose tiles remained a problem, even though engineers were able to dampen down the shock waves generated during blast-off.

On the positive side, the Canadian-built remote arm came out well from the trials, and several scientific packages were successfully operated from the cargo bay, including the first Getaway Special, a series of nine small experiments prepared by students from Utah State University. One of the most startling results, however, came from a radar system which 'uncovered' dry river beds and other landscape features long hidden beneath the North African sands.

THE SPACE TRUCK

During its gestation period, NASA had envisaged the Shuttle as a supply ship for a permanently orbiting space station. When financial constraints put an end to the station, the agency had to seek other ways of justifying the costs of constructing a reusable ship. From this dilemma arose the idea of a multi-purpose craft, capable of displacing expendable boosters as a satellite launch vehicle as well as carrying scientific equipment.

Unfortunately, the Shuttle's maximum altitude was about 500 miles (800 km) – much lower than the orbits required by most satellites. In order to attain their operational altitude of 22,375 miles (35,800 km), Shuttle-launched satellites had to carry their own rocket booster.

The first demonstration of this capability came with the STS-5 flight in November 1982 when two cylindrical communications satellites were deployed from cocoons inside Columbia's cargo bay. Set spinning at 50 rpm to stabilize their motion, both payloads were then spring-ejected, and their motors fired once they reached a safe distance from the Shuttle.

The limitations of this method of deployment surfaced in April 1983 during STS-6, the maiden flight of the Shuttle Challenger. Its main payload was a highly sophisticated Tracking and Data Relay Satellite (TDRS-A), the first of three such craft intended to act as orbital replacements for the large number of expensive ground relay stations.

Columbia lands on the desert runway at White Sands, New Mexico, at the end of the third Shuttle mission. (NASA)

A two-stage solid propellant motor was attached to fire the two-ton satellite into geostationary orbit. Although the first burn went satisfactorily, the second cut off prematurely, leaving TDRS-A in the wrong orbit. Several months went by before ground controllers were able to shift it to the correct location using its attitude control thrusters.

STS-6 was also notable for the first American spacewalks for nine years when Story Musgrave and Donald Peterson spent more than four hours cavorting in the cargo bay, watched by Commander Paul Weitz and pilot Karol Bobko. The new universal pressure suits should have been tried out on the previous flight but problems with a ventilator motor and a pressure regulator caused postponement of the EVA.

The next two missions by Challenger received most attention for their crew composition. On board STS-7 was America's first spacewoman, 32-year-old physicist Dr Sally Ride, while STS-8 carried the first American black astronaut, mission specialist Guion Bluford. Almost unnoticed on these five-crew expeditions were two physicians, Norman Thagard and William Thornton, who were assigned to conduct bio-medical experiments on themselves and other crew members in an effort to understand and combat space sickness.

SPACELAB

Despite the abandonment of the US space station concept in the early 1970s, NASA was determined to maintain some orbital research potential by placing a small module inside the Shuttle cargo bay. At the end of 1972, the European Space Research Organization (forerunner of the European Space Agency, ESA) agreed to participate in the Shuttle programme by developing such a research laboratory. The new facility was christened Spacelab.

A small, unpressurized Spacelab pallet had been carried in the cargo bay as early as STS-2, but the first opportunity to try out the complete laboratory did not arrive until STS-9 (also known as STS 41-A) in December 1983. In return for providing the hardware, ESA was allowed to

nominate its own payload specialist, so West German physicist Ulf Merbold became the first non-American astronaut.

One immediate change in routine came when the six-man crew was split into two shifts to enable 24-hour continuous work. The 'Red Team' comprised John Young (now aged 53 and taking part in a record sixth spaceflight), astronomer Robert Parker and Merbold, while the 'Blue Team' was made up of pilot Brewster Shaw, 53-year-old Skylab veteran Owen Garriott, and bio-medical specialist Byron Lichtenberg.

In an attempt to verify procedures for future Spacelabs, the crew carried out more than 70 experiments, ranging from life sciences to space physics and materials processing. The special requirements for some of these investigations led to Columbia flying an unusual 57 degree inclined orbit which carried it as far north as Denmark and as far south as the tip of Chile.

Their experimental work and frequent minor repair jobs were aided by a unique 'live' link via TDRS-A to scientists on the ground at the Johnson Space Center in Houston. So pleased were project managers with the results that they agreed to a one-day extension, bringing mission duration to a Shuttle record of ten days. Unfortunately, things were rather spoiled when a jolt from Columbia's thrusters knocked out two of the five onboard computers, and small fires broke out during landing as a result of fuel leaks in the tail section.

NASA made much of the fact that Spacelab hardware could be reused as often as 50 times over a lifespan of ten years. Yet, by early 1992 there had only been six further specialist missions of this type.

Spacelab 3 (actually the second to fly due to delays in completing the equipment for SL-2) in April 1985 carried a crew of seven – including three over 50 years of age – and two monkeys on a seven-day repeat of STS-9. The astronauts were not too happy when faeces escaped from the cages and began floating around the cabin! One of the two small 'Getaway Special' satellites was launched successfully, but a second stuck in its canister and had to be returned to Earth.

Spacelab 2 started with a chapter of disasters. Countdown on 12 July 1985 was cut short with just three seconds remaining to ignition when a valve refused to close. A two-week postponement meant that three of its primary experiments were badly affected by excess moonlight.

Even worse was to come when one of Challenger's engines overheated and had to be shut down. Then a sensor reading indicated a similar fault on another engine, threatening the first launch abort in the Shuttle's history. Ground controllers decided that the sensor was at fault and saved the mission by instructing the crew to override the computer. They eventually entered an orbit 70 miles (110 km) lower than planned.

This time, there was no pressurized laboratory on board. All the instruments were exposed in the cargo bay and controlled from the mid-deck by the crew. An ESA-built pointing system for four telescopes failed to live up to expectations, but the crew worked hard to put things right and earned an extra day in orbit. One of their more unusual experiments involved a taste test of Coca-Cola and Pepsi Cola packaged in special zero gravity cans.

Spacelab D-1 in October 1985 was the Shuttle's first chartered flight, with all the experiments provided by West Germany and mission management based in that country. Among the eight-person crew were two German payload specialists, Ernst Messerschmid and Reinhard Furrer, along with ESA astronaut Wubbo Ockels. During the seven-day voyage, the crew looked after a total of 75 experiments, some of which were improved versions of those previously tried.

Although the main emphasis was on the behaviour of fluids, crystals and metals in microgravity, there was one unusual item aboard. Measurements of astronauts' reactions to sudden movements were made as they sat on a sled attached to rails on Spacelab's floor. Ockels also tried out a new sleeping bag, choosing the pressurized laboratory for his bedroom instead of the mid-deck like his companions.

After an interlude of almost six years, the Spacelab Life Sciences 1 mission took place in June 1991, the first of its kind dedicated exclusively to research on the effects of weightlessness on humans and other living organisms. The

Who says being an astronaut is glamorous? Here German Payload Specialist Reinhard Furrer displays evidence of blood samples taken from his arm. The other arm visible at bottom right belongs to Dutch Payload Specialist Wubbo Ockels. Both men flew on the German-sponsored STS 61-A mission, also known as Spacelab D-1. (DFVLR/NASA)

crew of seven included three physicians, a chemist and a physicist. Apart from intensive monitoring of their own bodily adaptation to zero gravity, the astronauts studied changes in the muscles of rats and the ways in which jellyfish maintain their equilibrium.

The first International Microgravity Laboratory mission in January 1992 also carried a crew of seven, including Canadian researcher Roberta Bondar and ESA astronaut Ulf Merbold on his second Shuttle flight. Once again, there was an intensive programme of research into the physiological effects of zero gravity, including the use of a revolving chair. Other experiments included growth of exotic crystals and Earth observation. Each crew member took turns to wear a Los Angeles Dodgers baseball cap in memory of astronaut Manley (Sonny) Carter, who died in an airliner crash in 1991.

THE SPACE GARAGE

For more than 20 years after the first spacewalk, astronauts were confined to the vicinity of their ship by a variety of safety tethers and umbilicals which supplied oxygen and radio links. All of this changed in February 1984 when Bruce McCandless and Robert Stewart became the first spacewalkers to enjoy total freedom. The device which made this possible was an armchair-shaped backpack called a Manned Manoeuvring Unit (MMU).

Development of the MMU began many years earlier in the days of Gemini. Unfortunately, the unit was never used operationally, even though the Skylab astronauts were able to test-fly it inside their cavernous home. The version tested by the crew of STS 41-B weighed 310 lb (140 kg) on Earth and was designed to operate for up to six hours.

After a period of getting used to handling the bulky unit, McCandless moved out of the cargo bay to a distance of 300 feet (90 m) from Challenger. Stewart enjoyed a repeat perform-ance in a second 65-minute session of acrobatics. Using hand controls, the astronauts were able to fly in any direction, and even turn somersaults, by expelling nitrogen gas from 24 tiny thrusters.

At the end of their EVA on mission 41-B, McCandless tried using the remote arm as a movable work station, with his feet safely tucked into foot restraints. During a second spacewalk on the seventh day, the two astro-nauts practised ways of capturing a satellite using a platform installed in the cargo bay.

These activities were in preparation for the first satellite repair attempt on the next Shuttle flight, STS 41-C. One of the NASA's most important scientific satellites, an observatory

known as Solar Maximum Mission or Solar Max, had been largely inoperative after three fuses blew in its attitude control system in November 1980. Fortunately, Solar Max belonged to a new generation specifically designed for in-orbit servicing.

On the third day, Challenger commander Bob Crippen parked his ship within 200 feet (60 m) of the ailing giant, and George 'Pinky' Nelson donned his MMU along with a special capture device. Unfortunately, despite his best efforts, including manually grappling the huge satellite, he was unable to clamp the device onto a protruding pin. All he did succeed in doing was setting Solar Max tumbling. Efforts to grapple it with the robot arm proved impossible, and the situation was only saved when ground control-lers successfully stabilized the satellite once more.

Next day, Solar Max was hauled on board by the remote arm and locked into a special cradle in the cargo bay. Although hampered by their clumsy gloves, Nelson and James van Hoften managed to unbolt and replace the attitude control box, then open up the protective skin and fit a new electronics box. Lengthy checks by ground control after the refurbished satellite was released showed that the 'Ace Satellite Repair Co.' had done an excellent job.

It was not long before the MMU was again put to practical use. Both communications satellites deployed on mission 41-B were stuck in a useless, low orbit after their booster stages failed. Neither of them was equipped for a grappling recovery by the Shuttle remote arm, but NASA officials decided to attempt a rescue using the unique capabilities of the MMU.

On 12 November 1984, Joe Allen attached a specially designed 'stinger' to the front of his unit and flew across the 35-foot (10 m) gulf separating the orbiter Discovery from the slowly rotating Palapa satellite. By inserting the special docking device into its motor nozzle, Allen was able to bring the satellite under control and move it gingerly within range of the robot arm.

Unfortunately, Dale Gardner was unable to fit a bridge structure across the top of the satellite which the arm could grasp, so the 5 foot 6 inch tall Allen was obliged to perform a unique weightlifting act by holding the 1,200 lb (540 kg)

cylinder above his head while Gardner secured it in the bay.

This back-up procedure worked so well that the men decided to repeat the procedure for the Westar satellite. Two days later it was Gardner's turn to fly over to the errant satellite and bring it back to Allen, who then performed his Superman act all over again. After two magnificently successful six-hour EVAs, both multi-million-dollar breakdowns were safely installed in the cargo bay, ready for refurbishment back on Earth.

Yet another repair job was required after mission 51-D in April 1985. Although the first communications satellite deployed from Discovery operated perfectly, the second one refused to fire its motor. Examination from the orbiter showed that its 'sequence start' lever had stuck. After consultation with its manufacturers, NASA officials sanctioned a rescue attempt.

The astronauts fashioned two 'fly-swatters', but in order to attach them to the remote arm so that they would trip the lever, David Griggs and

Space rescue operation. Astronaut Dale Gardner uses his Manned Manoeuvring Unit (MMU) backpack to fly across to the ailing Westar VI satellite. By inserting a special 'stinger' into the end of the satellite, Gardner was able to return it to the Shuttle cargo bay for refurbishment back on Earth. (NASA)

Jeffrey Hoffman had to make the first totally unplanned EVA of the American space programme. Unfortunately, although Rhea Seddon was able to control the arm so that they repeatedly snagged it, the lever refused to budge. Further attempts to revive the dormant giant were postponed for four months until mission 51-I.

Hughes engineers came up with a risky repair routine which involved capturing the six and a half ton cylinder, bypassing the faulty switch and redeploying it for an automatic start controlled from the ground. Progress was slow due to a fault in the robot arm, but after a wrestling match lasting three hours, 'Ox' van Hoften and William Fisher had the satellite firmly under control. Now Fisher's surgical skills came to the fore as he began the bypass operation.

A second EVA the next day completed the work, and, with both men hanging onto the Syncom, they proceeded to spin it up and 'throw' it overboard. As Hughes President, Steve Dorfman, commented, it was 'the most remarkable salvage mission in the history of the space programme'.

Several Shuttle missions have been involved in preparations for a permanent space station due to be built in the late 1990s. As early as flight 12 (STS 41-D), a Shuttle crew demonstrated the ability to unfold a 102-foot (31 m) long solar array as an extra source of power. Space construction techniques were tested in November 1985 when Sherwood Spring and Jerry Ross spent two sessions erecting and dismantling a variety of tower and pyramid structures made from tubular beams.

On STS-37 in April 1991, astronauts Jerry Ross and Jay Apt stepped outside the airlock to test a number of transportation methods which could be used during space station assembly and maintenance. Asked to choose between several carts attached to a track along the side of the cargo bay, the men chose a manually propelled version over the electrical and mechanical designs.

THE END OF CHALLENGER

With the arrival of the fourth Shuttle, Atlantis, in October 1985, the fleet was complete. Hopes were high that NASA would be able to achieve a record 15 missions during 1986 on the way to achieving up to 30 flights a year by the end of the decade. Such was the agency's confidence in its hardware that non-specialist civilians were to be given seats on board the orbiters.

Political expediency and publicity extravaganzas had played an important role in NASA crew selection for some time. Apart from the various European astronauts who flew on Spacelab, the Shuttle had carried aloft a number of payload specialists from private companies as well as a Canadian, a Frenchman, a Mexican and a Saudi Arabian prince.

A new policy twist came in April 1985 when Senator Jake Garn, chairman of the committee which oversaw NASA's budget, was able to claim a seat aboard flight 51-D. Not to be outdone, Florida Congressman Bill Nelson, chairman of the House Space Science and Applications Committee, volunteered as a medical guinea pig for the first mission of 1986, STS 61-C. The next non-specialist to fly was Christa McAuliffe, who came out top of the pile in a competition to find a school teacher who would inspire the nation's youngsters. There was also much talk about who would be the first journalist in space.

Yet this confidence was misplaced. All was not well with the Shuttle, despite its record of 24 flights without a mishap. NASA had declared its Space Transportation System operational, even though 24 sorties for a new jet aircraft would never have qualified it as flightworthy. Most people ignored the fact that hardly any of the missions had lifted off on schedule, and quite a few had suffered potentially dangerous malfunctions, particularly prior to ignition or during launch.

Among the most troublesome pieces of hardware were the Shuttle main engines, which often had to be replaced at the end of a mission. Perhaps their most notable failure was on STS 41-D, the maiden flight of Discovery. The new Shuttle was four seconds from lift-off when a computer spotted that a fuel valve in main engine number three had not opened properly. Although the engines were shut down before the SRBs ignited, small fires broke out on the launch pad, almost leading to the first emergency evacuation of an American crew.

Further problems arose with the SRBs. On STS-8, for example, the lining of one of the solid fuel rocket boosters almost burned through, threatening to send the exhaust spewing out sideways and throwing Challenger into a spin. On mission 11 (STS 41-C), the SRBs' underperformance meant that the Shuttle nearly failed to reach orbital altitude.

At the same time as they were trying to look after and maintain the complex Shuttle technology, ground crews and flight directors were working under increased pressure to speed up the turn-around time and get the Shuttles flying

more regularly and frequently. Such pressures introduced the temptation to cut corners, and therein lay the downfall of the Shuttle programme.

The second launch planned for 1986 was STS 51-L, a mission notable for its payload of a TDRS satellite and the participation of Christa McAuliffe. In a typical pre-launch scenario, the lift-off date drifted from December 1985 towards the end of January. Bad weather intervened on the 26th, then a ground crew could not remove a handle on the side hatch, so the date shifted to the 28th.

During the night, temperatures dropped well below freezing, resulting in icicles on the launch gantry. After several checks and a couple of hours' delay next morning, the crew climbed aboard Challenger for the twenty-fifth Shuttle mission. It lasted just 73 seconds.

Unnoticed by anyone at the time, a small cloud of black smoke appeared beside one of the SRBs when ignition began. Heading out over the Atlantic, Challenger was buffeted by high winds and maximum aerodynamic stress, stretching the faulty seal in the SRB even further. Flames began to emerge like a blow torch from the side of the booster, eating into the giant fuel tank.

One of the struts which held the booster to the tank gave way, enabling the nose of the SRB to swivel and pierce the external tank. Liquid hydrogen and oxygen poured out through the gash in its side, only to be ignited in a huge ball of flame. Without any warning, the delta-winged orbiter was torn free and sent plunging into the ocean. Several of the crew tried using their emergency oxygen masks, but to no avail. All seven were dead by the time they hit the water.

Shuttle flights were immediately suspended as NASA and its contractors were publicly dissected by a Presidential Commission. Among the shocking revelations unveiled during the next few months was the fact that damage to the SRB seals had been noted on no less than 14 of the 24 previous missions. Even though these seals were listed as 'Criticality One' components

– liable to cause the loss of a craft if they failed – no one had suggested modifying their design. Experts also criticized the decision to launch in such low temperatures, despite reservations expressed at the time by some engineers.

Among the numerous recommendations made by the Rogers Commission were a complete review of 'Criticality One' components and safety procedures, including redesign of the SRB seals, and the creation of a crew escape system for use during launch.

Not surprisingly, with the Shuttle grounded for the next two years, ten of the astronaut corps decided to resign and take up challenges elsewhere. Among the changes at the top was the appointment of Admiral Richard Truly, former astronaut, as the agency's new administrator. His task was to reorganize the agency's managerial structure, restore morale, and oversee the construction of a replacement orbiter at the cost of $2.4 billion.

One further policy shift saw a change in emphasis for future Shuttle missions. No longer would the valuable orbiters and crew time be 'wasted' on launching payloads which could be carried on expendable boosters. Once existing commitments had been fulfilled, the fleet would concentrate on science missions and space station construction techniques.

RETURN TO ACTION

In an attempt to prevent similar disasters from recurring, every effort was made to ensure a safe return to operations. As a result, the twenty-sixth Shuttle flight was put back from February 1988 to June, and eventually to 29 September. Everyone breathed a long sigh of relief as Discovery cleared the tower and entered orbit, carrying an experienced five-man crew and the TDRS-C satellite. In a new departure from previous operational missions, the crew were obliged to wear pressure suits during launch and re-entry, but there were no mishaps in what was described as a 'flawless' mission.

Between STS-26 and January 1992 there were a further 19 Shuttle missions, mostly by the newer orbiters Discovery and Atlantis. With a fleet composed of only three vehicles, NASA was restricted to five missions during 1989 and six each in 1990 and 1991. Six of these were dedicated to deployment of heavy scientific satellites, some of which had been waiting many years in storage for their launch opportunity.

First to go was the Magellan radar mapping mission to Venus, sent on its way from the Shuttle cargo bay in May 1989. Five months later, it was the turn of Galileo to be sent on a lengthy, roundabout route to Jupiter. Prior to the loss of Challenger, NASA had intended to send Galileo direct to the giant planet by using a liquid-fuelled Centaur booster installed in the Shuttle cargo bay. This plan fell victim to the strict safety regulations introduced after the loss of Challenger. The Centaur had to be scrapped and replaced by a less powerful solid motor.

In April 1990, the long-awaited Hubble Space Telescope was carefully lifted by the remote arm from Discovery's cargo bay, but its performance was marred by the subsequent discovery of a flaw in its main mirror. Two more important science satellites followed with the deployment of the European-built solar probe, Ulysses, in October 1990 and the second of NASA's 'Great Observatories', the Gamma Ray Observatory, in April 1991.

Increased concern over pollution had led to calls for satellites to be used to monitor the environment. In response to this call, the six and a half ton Upper Atmosphere Research Satellite was launched from the Shuttle in September 1991 as the first stage in NASA's Mission To Planet Earth programme. Its primary aim was to study changes in the ozone layer, which shields us from harmful ultraviolet radiation.

Over the years, a significant number of Shuttle missions has been used either partially or wholly by the Department of Defense, starting with a classified Air Force payload on STS-4. Few details were ever officially released about these missions, and even the exact take-off time was hidden from the media prior to launch. Most of these missions seem to have involved deployment of large spy satellites and tests of 'Star Wars' equipment.

This veil of secrecy was finally lifted in April 1991 when the Air Force revealed that Discovery was carrying a small free-flying platform

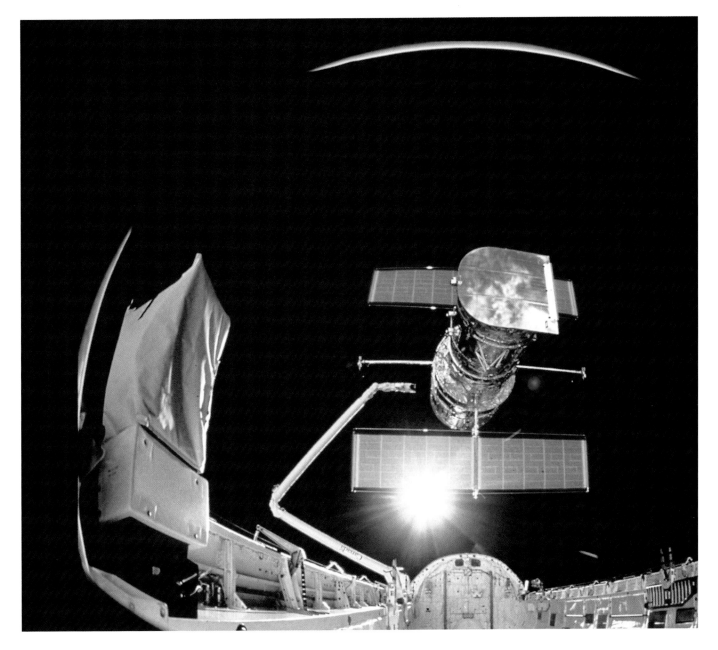

mounted with sensors which could eventually be used to detect enemy missiles. In another departure from normal DOD practice, the orbiter carried a large crew of seven (as expected, mostly military personnel) and stayed aloft for eight days instead of the usual three to five days.

The deployment of a large early warning satellite from STS-44 in November 1991 was also given wide coverage. However, the activities of military reconnaissance expert Thomas Hennen were curtailed when an inertial measurement unit failed, forcing Atlantis to return home three days early. Unfortunately, this is not the first indication that the Shuttle system remains

The Hubble Space Telescope, first of NASA's 'Great Observatories', is launched from the Shuttle cargo bay by the robot arm on 24 April 1990. The reflection of Earth's clouds is clearly visible on the telescope's protective outer door. (STSI/NASA)

flawed, despite the long run of successes since the return to flight operations.

In May 1990, a hydrogen leak was found in Columbia six hours before its planned launch of the Astro-1 observatory. When a similar leak was found in Atlantis a few weeks later, the entire fleet was grounded to allow an investigation. Although the two problems were even-

tually solved and were found to have different causes, no Shuttles were launched during a five-month spell that summer.

The spring of 1991 saw the postponement of STS-39 for seven weeks while engineers examined hairline cracks in the hinges of the propellant line doors on the orbiter Discovery. Similar cracks were found in the rest of the fleet, including the fifth Shuttle, Endeavour, which was still under construction!

Confidence was further eroded in May 1991 when, two days before the launch of STS-40, Rockwell International warned NASA that nine fuel temperature sensors on Columbia could be flawed. Subsequent investigation revealed that several were cracked, one seriously. Fragments from these sensors could have been sucked into the engines and possibly have destroyed the orbiter.

Even more disturbing, independent analysis of future prospects for the Shuttle fleet predicted that another orbiter would be lost before the end of the decade.

THE SOVIET SNOWSTORM

Until 15 November 1988, the United States was the only nation to possess a reusable spacecraft, although rumours had been circulating for many years that the Soviet Union was also developing its own Shuttle. The new vehicle, christened Buran (Snowstorm), should have made its grand appearance on 29 October, but the countdown was terminated one minute before ignition when a support arm was slow in uncoupling from the body of the launcher.

The second attempt went according to plan. On only its second test flight, the giant Energia rocket, Glushko's successor to the ill-fated N-1, blasted off from Baikonur with the delta-winged orbiter strapped onto its side. With such a

The Soviet Shuttle Buran awaits launch from Baikonur cosmodrome. Although similar in size and shape to the American Shuttle, Buran does not have its own rocket motors and relies on the giant Energia rocket to boost it into orbit. Note the long crew escape tunnel, not needed on this occasion because Buran's maiden flight was unmanned. (Space Commerce Corporation)

powerful rocket to provide the boost into orbit, there was no need for the Soviet Shuttle to carry its own advanced propulsion system.

Although the method of launch was totally different from that of the US orbiter, experts were not too surprised to note the numerous similarities in size and shape between Buran and its American counterpart. As early as 1984, claims had been circulating in the West that the Soviets had obtained copies of the 'blueprints' for the Space Shuttle.

In an effort to deflect some of this negative comment, the Soviets revealed that development studies for a winged orbiter had been undertaken in the mid-1960s, although work on Buran did not start until 1974, when Glushko replaced Mishin as Chief Designer. The project was originated by the Defence Ministry to counteract the military 'threat' from the US Shuttle.

The first group of Buran test pilots, led by Igor Volk, was selected in 1978. Four flights of a sub-scale spaceplane took place during 1982–84 under the Cosmos label. The following year, flight tests began with a full-size mock-up fitted with four jet engines. By the time Buran was launched three years later, 24 of these tests had been conducted, using both powered and unpowered landings.

What most impressed foreign observers about Buran's maiden flight was its ability to land automatically on the runway at Baikonur, only seven and a half miles (12 km) from its starting point, after two orbits and three and a half hours in space. It was clear, however, that the Soviet Shuttle had lost several protective tiles, and that it was not equipped with the safety and life support systems required for a manned mission.

Since that impressive debut, the programme has sunk into the doldrums. Three of the original 'Wolf pack' (named after Volk) had already died prior to the first flight, with a fourth fatality in September 1990. Even more significant has been the problem of funding – each mission costs several hundred million dollars – and failure to find a role for the new vehicle. As a result, no further launches of either Energia or Buran have taken place, leading to public complaints that the orbiter is simply a costly white elephant.

9

THE INVASION OF MARS?

A MIR TRANSITION

Even in times of political and economic stability, the art of forecasting is fraught with pitfalls. Following the dramatic collapse of the communist party in Eastern Europe and the break-up of the Soviet Union, together with economic recession and budgetary constraints in both the East and the West, how much more uncertain must be any attempts to predict the evolution of the space programme.

The desperate state of what was once the world's premier space power can be seen from the threats by cosmonauts to strike in early February 1992. Placards hanging in the flight control centre read, 'Cosmic prices and comic wages', despite a recent doubling of salaries. At the same time, Dr Polyakov complained that prices had skyrocketed and some foodstuffs for orbiting cosmonauts were no longer available. Meanwhile, Yuri Semenov, the inheritor of Korolev's design bureau, admitted that he would have either to make redundant thousands of employees or to concentrate on contracts for foreign customers.

This Russian eagerness to secure hard currency was evident even before the break-up of the Soviet Union. Since then a German has visited Mir in March 1992, followed by a third Soviet–French expedition in July. Further French missions are expected to take place at two-yearly intervals.

More recently, the European Space Agency and NASA have become paying customers. ESA astronaut Ulf Merbold spent 30 days on Mir in October 1994. The following year, Thomas Reiter became the first ESA representative to take walks in space during a six month stay aboard Mir. An agreement between the Russian and American space agencies was confirmed in June 1992. This led to two cosmonauts flying on the Shuttle in February 1994 and February 1995. The historic first docking between the Shuttle and Mir was completed in June 1995, when two cosmonauts and an American, Norman Thagard, were delivered to the Russian station. A further eight dockings are planned by 1998.

Although Dr Valeri Polyakov broke the world endurance record by staying in orbit from 8 January 1994 to 22 March 1995, a total of 439 days, future Russian missions are unlikely to exceed six months. These include flights with ESA, American, French and German astronauts before construction of the international Alpha station begins in 1997. Although a team of cosmonauts has been undergoing Buran flight training since 1978, the poor economic situation has meant that it has been placed in mothballs and is unlikely to fly again. The same probably applies to the giant Energia booster.

Further delays have hit the space station programme, and the Mir jigsaw will not now be completed before spring of 1996. The 20-ton Spektr (Spectrum) module eventually docked with Mir on 1 June 1995. When Priroda (Nature) arrives, the modules will be docked to Mir's front section, eventually splaying out at 90 degree intervals. Spektr will concentrate on geophysical studies while Priroda will be used for Earth remote sensing.

The Russians admit that the ageing Mir core will need replacing by 1998–9. A proposal to build a 100-ton Mir 2 space station, similar in concept to the American Alpha design, has been put to one side now that the Russians have agreed to join NASA, ESA, Canada and Japan in building the Alpha space station. The Russians will use old hardware as long as possible, but new modules dedicated to technology, medicine and biotechnology manufacturing may be launched later in the decade, along with man-tended free-flying factories.

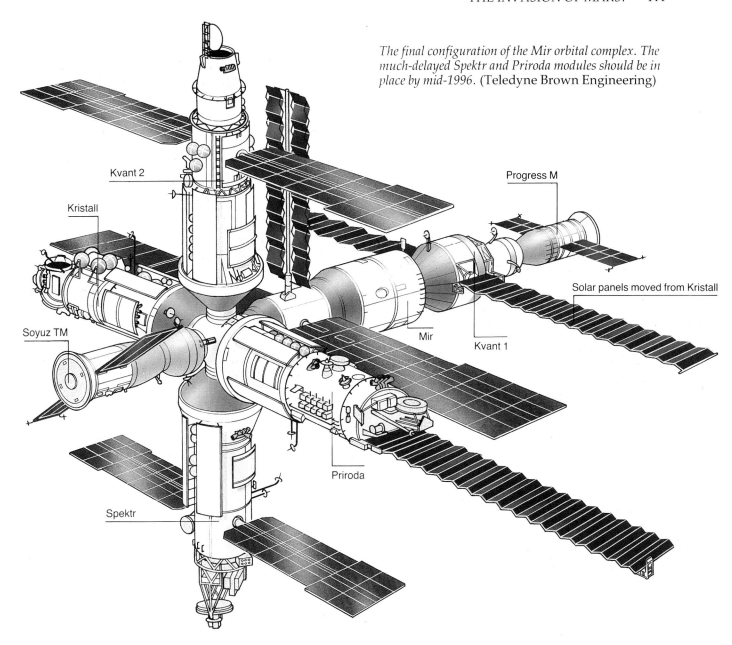

The final configuration of the Mir orbital complex. The much-delayed Spektr and Priroda modules should be in place by mid-1996. (Teledyne Brown Engineering)

Kvant 2

Kristall

Soyuz TM

Spektr

Priroda

Mir

Kvant 1

Progress M

Solar panels moved from Kristall

THE NEW ENDEAVOUR

In the United States, the 1990s will continue to be dominated by the Space Shuttle and the debate over the long-awaited permanent space station. A major step in the rehabilitation of the Shuttle programme took place on 25 April 1991 when Challenger's replacement, Endeavour, was rolled out to face the public. The fifth orbiter's maiden flight in May 1992 captured the imaginations of people all around the world as the crew struggled to retrieve a rogue Intelsat VI satellite and replace its kick motor. Only at the

third attempt, with a record three astronauts in the cargo bay holding on with all their might, was the mission accomplished.

Although it is two tons lighter than the first Shuttle, Columbia, it is a far more capable machine than its predecessors. Among these advances are more powerful onboard computers, improved navigation systems and auxiliary power units, and a drag chute to slow the craft on landing. The newcomer also carries extra fuel tanks, improved air conditioning and waste disposal facilities, and greater food storage capacity which will eventually enable it to remain in space for up to 28 days.

Now the fleet is restored to a full complement of four, NASA intends to increase the launch rate to eight per year. While the orbiters will continue to support international Spacelab missions, including the first Japanese manned mission in late 1992, most flights will be taken up with space science missions and assembly of the Alpha space station.

One of the most important missions set for 1993 was the refurbishment of the Hubble Space Telescope. A routine servicing visit turned into a major refitting exercise when astronauts installed an optical system which corrected the effects of the faulty mirror and replaced the giant solar panels, which vibrated every time they expanded and contracted.

NASA's plans for the Freedom space station came under a lot of fire from Congress and the scientific community. However, the scaled-down version shown in this artist's impression was later changed with the Alpha redesign in 1993. (NASA)

REDESIGNING FREEDOM

By the mid-1990s, a considerable amount of Shuttle activity should be devoted to the construction and maintenance of the Alpha space station, the first permanent American orbital structure of its kind. Since it was first conceived by the Reagan Administration in 1984, the station has undergone several major redesigns as Congress balked at the spiralling cost and unrealistic expectations.

By late 1990 it was clear that something radical had to be done: the station was nearly 30 per cent overweight, was underpowered, and would require 3,200 hours of maintenance by spacewalking astronauts, many times the total US EVA time. Even after major restructuring in April 1991, the space station was heavily criticized, particularly by the scientific community, who saw it as a bottomless pit into which government funds would be poured without any worthwhile recompense.

Construction of the $30 billion monolith should begin in 1997, but the assembly schedule is looking increasingly vulnerable. A programme to develop more powerful Shuttle SRBs has been cancelled, and no more than eight flights a year are planned for the foreseeable future. Half of these will be needed to deliver modules and other hardware to the Alpha station from 1997, once the Russian-built first sections are in place. A permanently manned station is not envisaged until the turn of the century, but even then, there will only be six occupants, less than the original number.

NASA maintains that Alpha may be extended during the next century to include further solar arrays, a second US laboratory and provision for extra crew members. By this time, it is expected that a new launch system will be available to replace the Shuttle.

International participation is one of the major features of the Alpha programme, but America's partners have been alarmed at the radical changes and lack of consultation which have marred the station's development. Nevertheless, the permanently manned structure should contain one Japanese and one European experimental module as well as a Canadian-built mobile servicing unit.

Both Japan and the European Space Agency (ESA) are also looking at ways of developing some autonomy in space transportation. At present, the Japanese are concentrating on an unmanned spaceplane called Hope which will transport equipment and supplies to the Japanese astronauts on board Alpha. The maiden launch of the 20-ton spaceplane is currently set for the year 2000, to be followed within a few years by a manned version.

At the end of 1992 ESA member states postponed a decision on whether to build a spaceplane called Hermes. ESA originally envisaged that three astronauts would participate in one Hermes mission a year to a free-flying laboratory. Like its Japanese counterpart, Hermes was intended to be launched on top of an expendable rocket, with an unmanned test flight in 2000 followed by a manned mission a year later.

Budget constraints have now caused the spaceplane project, and the free-flyer it was intended to service, to be abandoned. However, ESA pressed ahead with the recruitment of six astronauts in May 1992 to participate in joint manned missions with the USA and Commonwealth of Independent States. The agency hopes that it may eventually build a small, Apollo-type crew transfer vehicle.

SOARING INTO THE TWENTY-FIRST CENTURY

Unless there is a repeat of the Challenger disaster, no more Space Shuttles will be built. While the existing mixed fleet of Shuttles and expendable launch vehicles will continue to be important well into the first decade of the next century, they must eventually give way to a new space launch system which could complete its initial test flight as early as 1999.

The exact form which this new system will take is not yet known, but it will be expected to handle a range of medium to heavy payloads and be capable of evolutionary development as new mission requirements appear. In order to cut costs, the new launcher is likely to be based on components from the Shuttle and currently existing rockets. Its core section will use multiple units of a new liquid hydrogen–liquid oxygen engine, and different payload capabilities will be provided by various combinations of the core and strap-on boosters.

Looking further into the future, many countries are investigating rocket-powered single-stage-to-orbit launchers which will be highly reliable, fully reusable and capable of a turnaround within seven days. Various concepts are under consideration, including horizontal take-off and landing vehicles, as well as rockets which start and end their mission in a traditional vertical position.

Even more advanced are the aerospace planes which will eventually fly from a horizontal runway to orbit using hydrogen-fuelled, airbreathing engines during the early stages of ascent and only resorting to a rocket motor for the final transfer to orbit. Leading the way is America with its X-33 programme to develop a reusable single-stage launch vehicle, though no operational craft are yet planned.

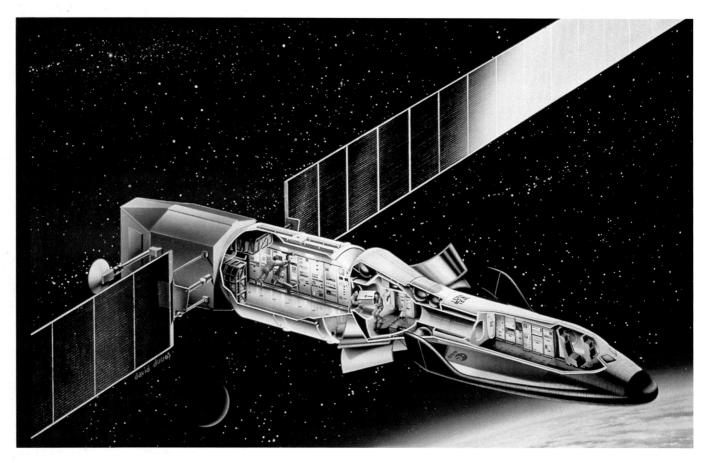

Above *Artist's impression of the European Hermes spaceplane docked with the Columbus Free Flying Laboratory in the first decade of the next century. (ESA) Hermes was cancelled in 1994.*

One of the more unusual proposals is the German Saenger project. A 150-ton hypersonic first stage will fly to an altitude of 22 miles (35 km), propelled first by turbojet engines, then by a liquid hydrogen turboramjet. At this point, either a manned or an unmanned Horus spaceplane will be launched from its back. The manned version will be able to carry four astronauts and three tons of payload to a space station, but will only have an orbital lifetime of 50 hours.

Another idea has evolved from joint Anglo-Soviet research into the use of a giant Antonov 225 aircraft. For the past few years, Soviet designers have been proposing using the plane as the 'first stage' carrier for a small spaceplane resting on top of a huge torpedo-shaped fuel tank. More recently, feasibility studies have been made for a British-built Hotol spaceplane

Artist's impression of the German two-stage Saenger spaceplane. The smaller Horus vehicle is released from the reusable first stage at an altitude of 22 miles (35 km), then proceeds under its own power to low Earth orbit.
(Deutsche Aerospace)

which would use Soviet rocket motors. The unmanned Hotol could be carried piggyback on the aircraft before separating and flying into orbit. At a later stage, the spaceplane's conventional rocket motors could be replaced by advanced airbreathing engines.

BACK TO THE MOON AND ON TO MARS

More than twenty years have passed since a human last set foot on the Moon. Many in the American aerospace community would argue that, since then, the world's leading space power has been rudderless, drifting with the financial tides and shifting political winds, despite President Reagan's attempt to generate new impetus by calling for a permanent space station within a decade.

On 20 July 1989, President Bush made a similar bid to revive national pride and provide NASA with a long-term commitment 'for the next century, back to the Moon . . . and this

Artist's impression of the first human mission to Mars in the year 2019. In the foreground, astronauts conduct scientific experiments as a dust storm approaches. The Mars landing vehicle in the background is their base during the surface excursion. The Martian moons Phobos and Deimos appear as bright stars in the twilight sky. (Ren Wicks/ NASA)

time to stay. And then a journey . . . to another planet, a manned mission to Mars.' He later went on to name a firm target date, the year 2019, which will be the fiftieth anniversary of Apollo 11.

So far, the response of Congress and the American people has been, at best, lukewarm. Few funds have been allocated to preliminary mission studies (although a series of low-cost missions to Mars have been scheduled for the late 1990s). A proposed orbital survey of the Moon's resources by a Lunar Observer spacecraft has submitted to the financial axe, although a small robot craft has been brought in to take its place.

Matters are even worse in the former Soviet Union. Financial stringency has forced scientists there to delay sending a Mars rover to the surface of the Red Planet and to ask foreign partners for financial support. Current plans call for a Mars-96 expedition to implant small weather stations and penetrators on the planet, but plans to send a balloon and roving vehicle for more detailed surface and atmospheric studies in 1998 have been scrapped.

When and how humans will return to the Moon, or progress outwards to Mars, are impossible to answer. At present, only the Russians have the practical experience and knowledge required to combat long-term weightlessness, and only the Russians possess a heavy-lift launch vehicle, Energia, capable of assembling a 500-ton Mars vehicle within a reasonably short space of time. On the other hand, their current economic turmoil will not evaporate overnight, and the only way in which this hardware will be put to use for a Mars mission is as part of an international co-operative venture.

Quite apart from the bio-medical and technological considerations in safely transporting humans to Mars, there is the question of finance. Conservative estimates put the cost of sending people to Mars at around $500 billion, 20 times the amount spent on the Apollo programme. Curiously, while the Soviets under President Gorbachev called openly for international co-operation to share expertise and cut costs, the United States continues to behave as if it, alone, can achieve the Mars landing.

In a recent report by a 'Synthesis Group' headed by former astronaut Tom Stafford, four possible mission scenarios were put forward. All of them involved a return to the Moon by the year 2005. During lengthy stays there, astronauts could test and validate equipment and procedures required for an expedition to Mars. At the same time, permanent bases could be established, complete with astronomical observatories and mining capacity.

Around 2012–14, two years before the explorers set off to bridge the 35 million mile (56 million km) gulf to Mars, a large nuclear-powered cargo ship would be sent on ahead to touch down at the planned landing site. When the crew arrive at their destination for an initial stay of anything from 30 to 100 days, their self-sufficient home and its pressurized roving vehicle would be ready and waiting to support their activities.

Although a journey to the Red Planet is feasible using traditional chemical propulsion, some form of nuclear power would be far preferable. Such advanced rockets have not yet been built, but their introduction would drastically cut the three-year round trip to Mars while reducing the spacecraft mass and providing greater operational flexibility.

What of the distant future? Does human destiny lie among the stars? Assuming that we are not so foolish as to destroy ourselves, and that economic growth can overcome competing demands for funds in an overpopulated, over-polluted world, the answer must be in the affirmative.

Already, American and Japanese companies are designing giant space ports, orbital hotels and colonies on other planets. There are no limits to human ingenuity and curiosity. Despite numerous setbacks, remarkable advances have already been made since the dawn of the Space Age, four decades ago. As the twenty-first century approaches, humanity will continue to look upwards and outwards, reaching for the stars. Now the end of the Cold War has opened the way to increased international cooperation.

APPENDIX 1

US MAN-RELATED SPACEFLIGHTS

> **NOTES:** Shuttle orbiters are identified by (A) Atlantis, (C) Columbia, (Ch) Challenger, (D) Discovery, (E) Endeavour, beside the mission designation.

Launch date	Mission	Crew
5.05.61	Mercury-Redstone 3	Shepard
21.07.61	Mercury-Redstone 4	Grissom
20.02.62	Mercury-Atlas 6	Glenn
24.05.62	Mercury-Atlas 7	Carpenter
3.10.62	Mercury-Atlas 8	Schirra
15.05.63	Mercury-Atlas 9	Cooper
23.03.65	Gemini 3	Grissom, Young
3.06.65	Gemini 4	McDivitt, White
21.08.65	Gemini 5	Cooper, Conrad
4.12.65	Gemini 7	Borman, Lovell
15.12.65	Gemini 6	Schirra, Stafford
16.03.66	Gemini 8	Armstrong, Scott
3.06.66	Gemini 9	Stafford, Cernan
18.07.66	Gemini 10	Young, Collins (M.)
12.09.66	Gemini 11	Conrad, Gordon
11.11.66	Gemini 12	Lovell, Aldrin
11.10.68	Apollo 7	Schirra, Eisele, Cunningham
21.12.68	Apollo 8	Borman, Lovell, Anders
3.03.69	Apollo 9	McDivitt, Scott, Schweickart
18.05.69	Apollo 10	Stafford, Young, Cernan
16.07.69	Apollo 11	Armstrong, Aldrin, Collins (M.)
14.11.69	Apollo 12	Conrad, Gordon, Bean
11.04.70	Apollo 13	Lovell, Swigert, Haise
31.01.71	Apollo 14	Shepard, Mitchell, Roosa
26.07.71	Apollo 15	Scott, Irwin, Worden
16.04.72	Apollo 16	Young, Mattingly, Duke
7.12.72	Apollo 17	Cernan, Evans, Schmitt
14.05.73	Skylab 1	—
25.05.73	Skylab 2	Conrad, Kerwin, Weitz
28.07.73	Skylab 3	Bean, Garriott, Lousma
16.11.73	Skylab 4	Carr, Gibson (E.), Pogue
15.07.75	Apollo 18 (ASTP)	Stafford, Brand, Slayton
12.04.81	STS-1 (C)	Young, Crippen
12.11.81	STS-2 (C)	Engle, Truly
22.03.82	STS-3 (C)	Lousma, Fullerton
27.06.82	STS-4 (C)	Mattingly, Hartsfield
11.11.82	STS-5 (C)	Brand, Overmyer, Allen (J.),Lenoir
4.04.83	STS-6 (Ch)	Weitz, Bobko, Peterson, Musgrave
18.06.83	STS-7 (Ch)	Crippen, Hauck, Ride, Fabian, Thagard

30.08.83	STS-8 (Ch)	Truly, Brandenstein, Gardner (D.), Bluford, Thornton (W.)
28.11.83	STS-9/41-A (C)	Young, Shaw, Garriott, Parker, Lichtenberg, Merbold
3.02.84	STS 41-B (Ch)	Brand, Gibson (R.), McCandless, McNair, Stewart
6.04.84	STS 41-C (Ch)	Crippen, Scobee, van Hoften, Hart, Nelson (G.)
30.08.84	STS 41-D (D)	Hartsfield, Coats, Resnik, Hawley, Mullane, Walker (C.)
5.10.84	STS 41-G (Ch)	Crippen, McBride, Ride, Sullivan, Leestma, Garneau, Scully-Power
8.11.84	STS 51-A (D)	Hauck, Walker (D.), Gardner (D.), Allen (J.) Fisher (A.)
24.01.85	STS 51-C (D)	Mattingly, Shriver, Onizuka, Buchli, Payton
12.04.85	STS 51-D (D)	Bobko, Williams, Seddon, Hoffman, Griggs, Walker (C.), Garn
29.04.85	STS 51-B (Ch)	Overmyer, Gregory, Lind, Thagard, Thornton (W.), van den Berg, Wang
17.06.85	STS 51-G (D)	Brandenstein, Creighton, Lucid, Fabian, Nagel, Baudry, Al-Saud
29.07.85	STS 51-F (Ch)	Fullerton, Bridges, Musgrave, Acton, England, Henize, Bartoe
27.08.85	STS 51-I (D)	Engle, Covey, van Hoften, Lounge, Fisher (W.)
3.10.85	STS 51-J (A)	Bobko, Grabe, Hilmers, Stewart, Pailes
30.10.85	STS 61-A (Ch)	Hartsfield, Nagel, Buchli, Bluford, Dunbar, Furrer, Messerschmid, Ockels
26.11.85	STS 61-B (A)	Shaw, O'Connor, Cleave, Spring, Ross, Neri-Vela, Walker (C.)
12.01.86	STS 61-C (C)	Gibson (R.), Bolden, Chang-Diaz, Hawley, Nelson (G.), Cenker, Nelson (W.)
28.01.86	STS 51-L (Ch)	Scobee, Smith, Resnik, Onizuka, McNair, Jarvis, McAuliffe
29.09.88	STS-26 (D)	Hauck, Covey, Hilmers, Lounge, Nelson (G.)
2.12.88	STS-27 (A)	Gibson (R.), Gardner (G.), Mullane, Shepherd, Ross
13.03.89	STS-29 (D)	Coats, Blaha, Buchli, Springer, Bagian
4.05.89	STS-30 (A)	Walker (D.), Grabe, Thagard, Cleave, Lee
8.08.89	STS-28 (C)	Shaw, Richards, Adamson, Leestma, Brown (M.)
18.10.89	STS-34 (A)	Williams, McCulley, Chang-Diaz, Lucid, Baker (E.)
22.11.89	STS-33 (D)	Gregory, Blaha, Carter, Musgrave, Thornton (K.)
9.01.90	STS-32 (C)	Brandenstein, Wetherbee, Dunbar, Ivins, Low
28.02.90	STS-36 (A)	Creighton, Casper, Thuot, Mullane, Hilmers
24.04.90	STS-31 (D)	Shriver, Bolden, Hawley, Sullivan, McCandless
6.10.90	STS-41 (D)	Richards, Cabana, Melnick, Shepherd, Akers
15.11.90	STS-38 (A)	Covey, Culbertson, Gemar, Meade, Springer
2.12.90	STS-35 (C)	Brand, Gardner (G.), Hoffman, Lounge, Parker, Durrance, Parise
5.04.91	STS-37 (A)	Nagel, Cameron, Godwin, Ross, Apt
28.04.91	STS-39 (D)	Coats, Hammond, Harbaugh, McMonagle, Bluford, Veach, Hieb

5.06.91	STS-40 (C)	O'Connor, Gutierrez, Bagian, Jernigan, Seddon, Gaffney, Hughes-Fulford
2.08.91	STS-43 (A)	Blaha, Baker (M.), Lucid, Low, Adamson
12.09.91	STS-48 (D)	Creighton, Reightler, Gemar, Buchli, Brown (M.)
24.11.91	STS-44 (A)	Gregory, Henricks, Voss, Musgrave, Runco, Hennen
22.01.92	STS-42 (D)	Grabe, Oswald, Thagard, Readdy, Hilmers, Bondar, Merbold
24.03.92	STS-45 (A)	Bolden, Duffy, Sullivan, Leestma, Foale, Frimout, Lichtenberg
7.05.92	STS-49 (E)	Brandenstein, Chilton, Melnick, Thuot, Hieb, Thornton (K.), Akers
25.06.92	STS-50 (C)	Richards, Bowersox, Dunbar, Baker (E.), Meade, DeLucas, Trinh
31.07.92	STS-46 (A)	Shriver, Allen (A.), Hoffman, Ivins, Chang-Diaz, Nicollier, Malerba
12.09.92	STS-47 (E)	Gibson (R.), Brown (C.), Lee, Apt, Davis, Mohri, Jemison
22.10.92	STS-52 (C)	Wetherbee, Baker (M.), Jernigan, Shepherd, Veach, MacLean
2.12.92	STS-53 (D)	Walker (D.), Cabana, Bluford, Clifford, Voss (J.S.)
13.01.93	STS-54 (E)	Casper, McMonagle, Harbaugh, Helms, Runco
8.04.93	STS-56 (D)	Cameron, Oswald, Cockrell, Foale, Ochoa
26.04.93	STS-55 (C)	Nagel, Henricks, Precourt, Ross, Harris, Schlegel, Walter
21.06.93	STS-57 (E)	Grabe, Duffy, Low, Voss (J.E.), Sherlock, Wisoff
12.09.93	STS-51 (D)	Culbertson, Readdy, Bursch, Newman, Walz
18.10.93	STS-58 (C)	Blaha, Searfoss, Seddon, MacArthur, Wolf, Lucid, Fettman
2.12.93	STS-61 (E)	Covey, Bowersox, Musgrave, Nicollier, Thornton, Akers, Hoffman, Harbaugh
3.02.94	STS-60 (D)	Bolden, Reightler, Krikalev, Davis, Chang-Diaz, Sega
4.03.94	STS-62 (C)	Casper, Allen (A.), Thuot, Gemar, Ivins
9.04.94	STS-59 (E)	Gutierrez, Chilton, Godwin, Apt, Clifford, Jones
8.07.94	STS-65 (C)	Cabana, Halsell, Hieb, Chiao, Thomas, Mukai, Walz
9.09.94	STS-64 (D)	Richards, Hammond, Meade, Lee, Helms
30.09.94	STS-68 (E)	Baker (M.), Wilcutt, Jones, Smith, Wisoff, Bursch
3.11.94	STS-66 (A)	McMonagle, Brown, Parazynski, Ochoa, Clervoy, Tanner
3.02.95	STS-63 (D)	Wetherbee, Collins (E.), Titov, Foale, Voss-Ford, Harris
2.03.95	STS-67 (E)	Oswald, Gregory, Lawrence, Parise, Durrance, Jernigan, Grunsfeld
27.06.95	STS-71 (A)	Gibson (R.), Precourt, Baker (E.), Harbaugh, Dunbar, Solovyev, Budarin
13.07.95	STS-70 (D)	Henricks, Kregel, Sherlock, Thomas, Weber
7.09.95	STS-69 (E)	Walker, Cockrell, Voss (J.S.), Newman, Gernhardt
20.10.95	STS-73 (C)	Bowersox, Rominger, Thornton, Coleman, Sacco, Lopez-Alegria, Leslie
12.11.95	STS-74 (A)	Cameron, Halsell, Ross, McArthur, Hadfield

Bruce McCandless during the first tests of the Manned Manoeuvring Unit, Shuttle Mission 41-B, 7 February 1984. (NASA)

APPENDIX 2

SOVIET/RUSSIAN MAN-RELATED SPACEFLIGHTS

NOTES:
(a) Alexander Alexandrov (1) is a Russian, while (2) is Bulgarian
(b) ? denotes planned launch dates and crews at the time of writing.
(c) All STS flights are American shuttle flights to the Russian Mir space station.

Launch date	Mission	Crew
12.04.61	Vostok 1	Gagarin
6.08.61	Vostok 2	Titov (G.)
11.08.62	Vostok 3	Nikolayev
12.08.62	Vostok 4	Popovich
14.06.63	Vostok 5	Bykovsky
16.06.63	Vostok 6	Tereshkova
12.10.64	Voskhod 1	Komarov, Feoktistov, Yegorov
18.03.65	Voskhod 2	Leonov, Belyayev
23.04.67	Soyuz 1	Komarov
25.10.68	Soyuz 2	
26.10.68	Soyuz 3	Beregovoi
14.01.69	Soyuz 4	Shatalov
15.01.69	Soyuz 5	Volynov, Yeliseyev, Khrunov
11.10.69	Soyuz 6	Shonin, Kubasov
12.10.69	Soyuz 7	Filipchenko, Volkov (V.), Gorbatko
13.10.69	Soyuz 8	Shatalov, Yeliseyev
1.06.70	Soyuz 9	Nikolayev, Sevestyanov
19.04.71	Salyut 1	—
23.04.71	Soyuz 10	Shatalov, Yeliseyev, Rukavishnikov
6.06.71	Soyuz 11	Dobrovolsky, Volkov (V.), Patsayev
3.04.73	Salyut 2	—
11.04.73	Cosmos 557	—
27.09.73	Soyuz 12	Lazarev, Makarov
18.12.73	Soyuz 13	Klimuk, Lebedev
25.06.74	Salyut 3	—
3.07.74	Soyuz 14	Popovich, Artyukhin
26.08.74	Soyuz 15	Sarafanov, Demin
2.12.74	Soyuz 16	Filipchenko, Rukavishnikov
26.12.74	Salyut 4	—
11.01.75	Soyuz 17	Gubarev, Grechko
5.04.75	Soyuz 18-1	Lazarev, Makarov
24.05.75	Soyuz 18	Klimuk, Sevestyanov
15.07.75	Soyuz 19 (ASTP)	Leonov, Kubasov
17.11.75	Soyuz 20	—
22.06.76	Salyut 5	—
6.07.76	Soyuz 21	Volynov, Zholobov
15.09.76	Soyuz 22	Bykovsky, Aksyonov
14.10.76	Soyuz 23	Zudov, Rozhdestvensky
7.02.77	Soyuz 24	Gorbatko, Glazkov

121

29.09.77	Salyut 6	—
9.10.77	Soyuz 25	Kovalyonok, Ryumin
10.12.77	Soyuz 26	Romanenko, Grechko
10.01.78	Soyuz 27	Dzhanibekov, Makarov
20.01.78	Progress 1	—
2.03.78	Soyuz 28	Gubarev, Remek
15.06.78	Soyuz 29	Kovalyonok, Ivanchenkov
27.06.78	Soyuz 30	Klimuk, Hermaszewski
7.07.78	Progress 2	—
8.08.78	Progress 3	—
26.08.78	Soyuz 31	Bykovsky, Jahn
4.10.78	Progress 4	—
25.02.79	Soyuz 32	Lyakhov, Ryumin
12.03.79	Progress 5	—
10.04.79	Soyuz 33	Rukavishnikov, Ivanov
13.05.79	Progress 6	—
6.06.79	Soyuz 34	—
28.06.79	Progress 7	—
16.12.79	Soyuz T-1	—
27.03.80	Progress 8	—
9.04.80	Soyuz 35	Popov, Ryumin
27.04.80	Progress 9	—
26.05.80	Soyuz 36	Kubasov, Farkas
5.06.80	Soyuz T-2	Malyshev, Aksyonov
29.06.80	Progress 10	—
23.07.80	Soyuz 37	Gorbatko, Tuan
18.09.80	Soyuz 38	Romanenko, Tamayo-Mendez
28.09.80	Progress 11	—
27.11.80	Soyuz T-3	Kizim, Makarov, Strekalov
24.01.81	Progress 12	—
12.03.81	Soyuz T-4	Kovalyonok, Savinykh
22.03.81	Soyuz 39	Dzhanibekov, Gurragcha
25.04.81	Cosmos 1267	—
14.05.81	Soyuz 40	Popov, Prunariu
19.04.82	Salyut 7	—
13.05.82	Soyuz T-5	Berezovoi, Lebedev
23.05.82	Progress 13	—
24.06.82	Soyuz T-6	Dzhanibekov, Ivanchenkov, Chrétien
10.07.82	Progress 14	—
19.08.82	Soyuz T-7	Popov, Serebrov, Savitskaya
17.09.82	Progress 15	—
31.10.82	Progress 16	—
2.03.83	Cosmos 1443	—
20.04.83	Soyuz T-8	Titov (V.), Strekalov, Serebrov
27.06.83	Soyuz T-9	Lyakhov, Alexandrov (1)
17.08.83	Progress 17	—
27.09.83	Soyuz T-10-1	Titov (V.), Strekalov
20.10.83	Progress 18	—
8.02.84	Soyuz T-10	Kizim, Solovyov (V.), Atkov
21.02.84	Progress 19	—

3.04.84	Soyuz T-11	Malyshev, Strekalov, Sharma
15.04.84	Progress 20	—
8.05.84	Progress 21	—
28.05.84	Progress 22	—
17.07.84	Soyuz T-12	Dzhanibekov, Savitskaya, Volk
14.08.84	Progress 23	—
6.06.85	Soyuz T-13	Dzhanibekov, Savinykh
21.06.85	Progress 24	—
19.07.85	Cosmos 1669	—
17.09.85	Soyuz T-14	Vasyutin, Grechko, Volkov (A.)
27.09.85	Cosmos 1686	—
20.02.86	Mir	—
13.03.86	Soyuz T-15	Kizim, Solovyov (V.)
19.03.86	Progress 25	—
23.05.86	Progress 26	—
21.05.86	Soyuz TM-1	—
16.01.87	Progress 27	—
6.02.87	Soyuz TM-2	Romanenko, Laveikin
3.03.87	Progress 28	—
31.03.87	Kvant 1	—
21.04.87	Progress 29	—
19.05.87	Progress 30	—
22.07.87	Soyuz TM-3	Viktorenko, Alexandrov (1), Faris
3.08.87	Progress 31	—
23.09.87	Progress 32	—
20.11.87	Progress 33	—
21.12.87	Soyuz TM-4	Titov (V.), Manarov, Levchenko
20.01.88	Progress 34	—
23.03.88	Progress 35	—
13.05.88	Progress 36	—
7.06.88	Soyuz TM-5	Solovyov (A.), Savinykh, Alexandrov (2)
18.07.88	Progress 37	—
29.08.88	Soyuz TM-6	Lyakhov, Polyakov, Mohmand
9.09.88	Progress 38	—
26.11.88	Soyuz TM-7	Volkov (A.), Krikalev, Chrétien
25.12.88	Progress 39	—
10.02.89	Progress 40	—
16.03.89	Progress 41	—
23.08.89	Progress M-1	—
5.09.89	Soyuz TM-8	Viktorenko, Serebrov
26.11.89	Kvant 2	—
20.12.89	Progress M-2	—
11.02.90	Soyuz TM-9	Solovyov (A.), Balandin
28.02.90	Progress M-3	—
5.05.90	Progress 42	—
31.05.90	Kristall	—
1.08.90	Soyuz TM-10	Manakov, Strekalov
15.08.90	Progress M-4	—
27.09.90	Progress M-5	—
2.12.90	Soyuz TM-11	Afanasyev, Manarov, Akiyama

14.01.91	Progress M-6	—
19.03.91	Progress M-7	—
18.05.91	Soyuz TM-12	Artsebarski, Krikalev, Sharman
30.05.91	Progress M-8	—
21.08.91	Progress M-9	—
2.10.91	Soyuz TM-13	Volkov (A.), Viehboeck, Aubakirov
17.10.91	Progress M-10	—
25.01.92	Progress M-11	—
17.03.92	Soyuz TM-14	Viktorenko, Kaleri, Flade
20.04.92	Progress M-12	—
30.06.92	Progress M-13	—
27.07.92	Soyuz TM-15	Solovyov (A.), Avdeyev, Tognini
16.08.92	Progress M-14	—
27.10.92	Progress M-15	—
24.01.93	Soyuz TM-16	Manakov, Polishchuk
21.02.93	Progress M-16	—
31.03.93	Progress M-17	—
22.05.93	Progress M-18	—
1.07.93	Soyuz TM-17	Tsiblyev, Serebrov, Haignere
11.08.93	Progress M-19	—
12.10.93	Progress M-20	—
8.01.94	Soyuz TM-18	Afanasyev, Usachev, Polyakov
28.01.94	Progress M-21	—
22.03.94	Progress M-22	—
22.05.94	Progress M-23	—
1.07.94	Soyuz TM-19	Malenchenko, Musabayev
25.08.94	Progress M-24	—
4.10.94	Soyuz TM-20	Viktorenko, Kondakova, Merbold
11.11.94	Progress M-25	—
15.02.95	Progress M-26	—
14.03.95	Soyuz TM-21	Dezhurov, Strekalov, Thagard
9.04.95	Progress M-27	—
20.05.95	Spektr	—
27.06.95	STS-71 (Atlantis)	Solovyov, Budarin + US crew
20.07.95	Progress M-28	—
3.09.95	Soyuz TM-22	Gidzenko, Avdeyev, Reiter
8.10.95	Progress M-29	—
12.11.95	STS-74 (Atlantis)	US Crew
18.12.95	Progress M-30	—
21.02.96?	Soyuz TM-23	Onufriendko, Usachev
10.03.96?	Priroda	—
21.03.96?	STS-76 (Atlantis)	US Crew
1.04.96?	Progress M-31	—
1.06.96?	Progress M-32	—
6.07.96?	Soyuz TM-24	Andre-Deshays, Manakov, Vinogradov
27.07.96?	Progress M-33	—
1.08.96?	STS-79 (Atlantis)	US Crew
15.10.96?	Progress M-34	—
9.12.96?	Soyuz TM-25	Tsiblyev, Lazutkin, Ewald

INDEX